THE OFFICIAL LIVERPOOL FC CROSSWORD BOOK

First published in Great Britain in 2004 by
Carlton Books,
20 Mortimer Street,
London W1T 3JW

10 9 8 7 6 5 4 3 2 1

ISBN 1 84442 674 2

Editorial manager: Martin Corteel
Editorial assistant: David Ballheimer
Design: Darren Jordan
Production: Lisa French

Printed in Great Britain

THE OFFICIAL **LIVERPOOL FC** CROSSWORD BOOK

50 CROSSWORD PUZZLES TOTALLY DEVOTED TO THE MIGHTY REDS

Compiled by Thomas Trickett

Introduction

Welcome to the *Official Liverpool FC Crossword Book.*

Here you will find a collection of 50 crossword puzzles which will tax the minds of the most ardent Liverpool fans. The clues have been designed to test, and even expand, your knowledge of your favourite football club. We have sought to appeal to every generation of puzzler by providing clues that give answers that range back to the earliest days right up to the present day, delving into Liverpool's illustrious history.

The clues range from the reasonably straightforward – requiring the names of individual players – to more specialist ones, asking for players' nicknames or future or past clubs. There are playful posers in which the answer is hidden in the clue and anagrams which require unscrambling. If you are determined to solve every clue of every puzzle, you will find it useful to have a couple of reference books at your side. Most of the answers can be found in either *The Official Liverpool FC Illustrated History* or *The Official Liverpool FC Illustrated Encyclopedia,* both published by Carlton Books.

The puzzles come from the rich heritage which makes Liverpool FC the remarkable club it is or from the wider world of football as well as a few general questions about the city and its characters. All facts and figures are as of the end of the 2003–04 FA Barclaycard Premiership season.

Thomas Trickett

Acknowledgements

We would like to express our thanks to Mr Keith Davis for his invaluable technical skill in the creation of this book. A special mention must also go to Mr Paul Windle, whose expertise and advice regarding Liverpool FC has made this book easier for the Thomas Trickett team to complete. Other acknowledgements go to our Sport Consultant, Mr Arthur Llewellyn, whose incredibly wide knowledge of sports has helped this project go according to plan. Assistant researchers Nathalie Antonia Llewellyn, Louise Gould and Nuala Alys also deserve recognition for the alacrity with which they dealt with the occasional obstacles that arose.

The Crosswords

Crossword No. 1

Across

1 Liverpool boss, 1974–83 (3, 7)
8 James – – – – – – –, 1930s/40s Liverpool player, later Secretary, who died in tragic circumstances (7)
9 – – – – – Irwin, Liverpool defender, 1974–81 (5)
10 Widzew – – – – knocked out Liverpool in 1983 European Cup quarter-finals (4)
11 Stig-– – – – Bjornebye, 1990s Liverpool and Norway defender (4)
12 1981 European Cup Final result: Liverpool 1, Real Madrid – – – (3)
14 Colin – – – – – –, Everton boss when Kenny Dalglish was boss at Liverpool (6)
15 Surname of midfielder who joined Liverpool from Newcastle United in 1999 (6)
18 – – – John Smith, Liverpool chairman, 1973–90 (3)
20 Football law, like away goals in Europe (4)
21 Roger – – – –, Liverpool's 1966 England World Cup winning forward (4)
23 – – – – – Blenkinsop, 1930s Liverpool and England full-back (5)
24 Ex-Reds keeper Brad Friedel hails from United States of – – – – – – – (7)
25 River team where Liverpool play (10)

Down

1 Played an extraordinary good game (slang) (7)
2 Suspensions (4)
3 Missing from training! (6)
4 In 1989 John Aldridge left Liverpool for Real – – – – – – – – (8)
5 – – – – – Hughes, former Liverpool captain (5)
6 Striker joined Liverpool from Leicester City, 2000 (5, 6)
7 Michael Owen is a star of the – – – – – – – – – – – – – (7, 4)
13 The nickname of team Bill Shankly managed 1956–59 (8)
16 Type of language may result in sending-off (7)
17 David –'– – – – –, ex-Leeds United boss who bought Robbie Fowler in 2001 (1'5)
19 It's strange the Reds find the goal out of shooting reach, apparently (5)
22 Half a circle found on football pitch (4)

LIVERPOOL

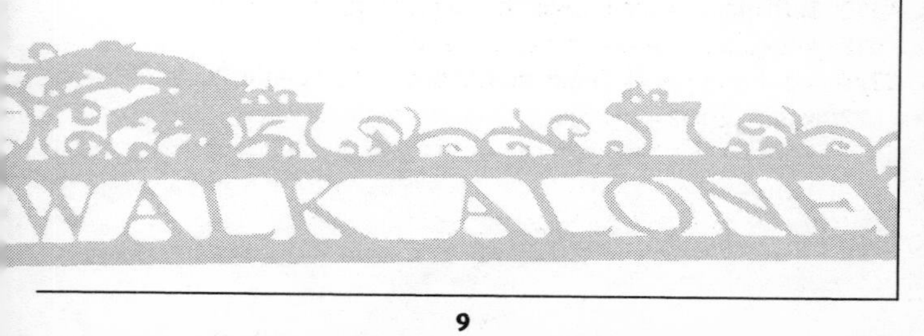
WALK ALONE

Crossword No. 2

Across

1 --- -- John, former Reds forward (3, 2)
4 Long stretch for each Reds keeper, apparently (5)
10 Italian side who knocked out the Reds, 1965 European Cup semi-final (5)
11 Famous city-centre hotel in Liverpool (7)
12 Steve --------, 1980s/90s Reds defender (8)
13 -----Heinz Riedle, 1990s Reds striker (4)
15 Liverpool's 1972–73 League title was their ------ (6)
17 Grab the title, maybe! (6)
19 Alter Roma for Ian Rush's nickname (anag) (4)
20 Craig --------, 1980s Reds midfielder (8)
23 Kevin Keegan played for this country (7)
24 Midfielder Ian Callaghan was born on 10 ----- 1942 (5)
25 John Houlding was the original ----- of Anfield (5)
26 Chelsea or Birmingham City nickname, definitely not Reds (5)

Down

2 Another professional name for a player that pretends to be fouled (5)
3 1960s/70s Liverpool player Geoff Strong shows his might! (8)
5 Steven Gerrard is not an odd player, apparently (4)
6 Alan Hansen was Reds ------- in the mid-1980s (7)
7 Chester-born striker who joined the Reds as a trainee, first game 1997 (7, 4)
8 Mike -----, ex-Reds midfielder went to West Ham as a swap (5)
9 Liverpool manager 1959–74 (4, 7)
14 The Reds tried to sign 1966 England World Cup winning midfielder (4, 4)
16 Birth city of Kenny Dalglish (7)
18 Nickname of Ron Yeats (5)
21 Amount of goals in a hat-trick (5)
22 Football crowd movement known as the Mexican ---- (4)

■	1	2		3		■	4	5		6		■
7	■		■		■	8	■		■		■	9
10					■	11						
	■		■		■		■		■		■	
12								■	13			
	■	■	■		■		■	14	■		■	
15		16				■	17					
	■		■		■	18	■		■	■	■	
19				■	20					21		
	■		■	22	■		■		■		■	
23							■	24				
	■		■		■		■		■		■	
■	25					■	26					■

Crossword No. 3

Across

1 Legendary ex-Liverpool and Wales goalscorer (3, 4)
7 2000s, Reds midfielder El Hadji Diouf was born in - - - - -, Senegal (5)
8 Not the closing goal! (7)
9 - - - - - - Hannah, one of the Evertonians in the first-ever Liverpool team (6)
11 Jan Molby was a regular penalty- - - - - - for Liverpool (5)
13 Go through the turnstiles to - - - - admittance (4)
14 In 1906 Anfield stadium had the largest in England (7)
15 They are changed after half-time (4)
16 Gordon - - - - -, 1960s Liverpool and England midfielder (5)
17 An educational period in football training, perhaps! (6)
21 www.liverpoolfc.tv, for instance (7)
22 Jerzy - - - - -, Polish keeper who joined Liverpool 2001 (5)
23 Peter Thompson played - - - - - - - -left for Liverpool 1963–74 (7)

Down

2 Robbie Fowler made his first for Liverpool in 1993 (10)
3 Ex-Liverpool captain nicknamed "Rowdy" (3, 5)
4 Rigobert, former Liverpool defender (4)
5 John Barnes hides farm building, apparently (4)
6 David - - - -clough, ex-Liverpool striker and "Supersub" (4)
9 Take the lead and you are! (5)
10 Knocked out of a competition! (10)
12 - - - - - Kettle, 1970s/80s Liverpool defender (5)
13 As goalscorers, Ian Rush and Roger Hunt could be described thus! (8)
18 Percy - - - -, 1900s Reds full-back, though not biblical King! (4)
19 Michael - - - -, 1990s/2000s Liverpool striker (4)
20 Food price list often autographed by Liverpool players (4)

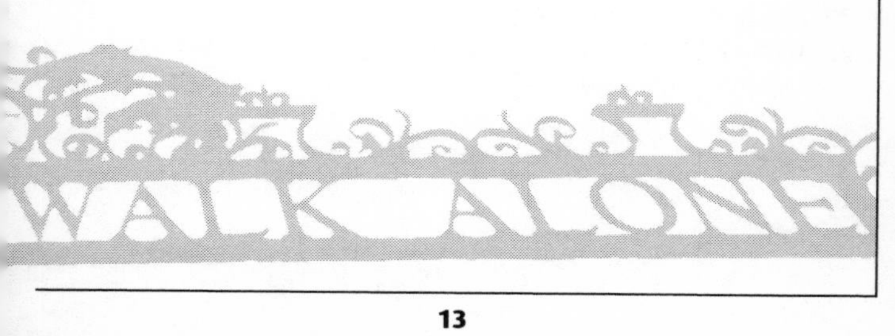
WALK ALONE

Crossword No. 4

Across

1 Dressing spaces at Anfield (5)
7 Football lout (8)
8 Position just inside the top ten (5)
10 1960s/70s, Liverpool defender (5, 5)
12 Liverpool last won the - - - - - - - - Cup in 1984 (8)
14 - - - - Pen, was a fenced in enclosure at Anfield for kids (4)
16 The sort of ball a goalkeeper plucks out of the air (4)
17 Participant in the last game of a cup competition (8)
20 Gary - - - - - - - - - - -, Motherwell-born Liverpool midfielder 2000–2002 (10)
23 - - - - - Hunt, Liverpool's leading goalscorer of the 1960s (5)
24 All football shirts are! (8)
25 David - - - - -, ex-Liverpool goalkeeper (5)

Down

1 - - - - - - Whelan, played 493 games for Liverpool (6)
2 - - - - McQueen, Liverpool manager 1923–28 (4)
3 From playing bad Liverpool are in good shape (anag) (4)
4 The facilities at Anfield are first-- - - - - - (5)
5 Steve - - - - - - - - - -, keeper kept out by Ray Clemence, who starred at Coventry (9)
6 A goal measures 288 x 96 of them (6)
9 Design pattern on 1950s Liverpool socks (5)
11 Matchday publication (9)
13 Go via Israel to find ex-Reds defender, - - - Cohen (anag) (3)
15 Material for matchday programme (5)
16 Liverpool 1990s/2000s German midfielder (6)
18 Star sign of Graeme Souness (6)
19 Change inside Mark Walters, apparently (5)
21 1990s Reds striker Paul Stewart likes hot food, apparently (4)
22 Liverpool have never lost against the Italian side from the Stadio Olimpico (4)

YOU'LL NEVER WALK ALONE
LIVERPOOL
FOOTBALL CLUB
EST 1892

Crossword No. 5

Across

6 Liverpool central midfielder 1972–76 (5, 7)
8 Liverpool have played this German side three times and drawn each game (7)
9 Name team strives to win (5)
10 Alter team to find friend (anag) (4)
12 ------ Bennett, original member of the "Boot Room" staff at Anfield (6)
14 Penalties can be scored, missed or ----- (5)
15 Cleared ball with the foot (6)
16 ---- Diarra, French midfielder signed for Liverpool 2002 (4)
19 Arrests a worn out player, apparently (5)
21 Whilst with Liverpool Jamie Redknapp spent a long time out ------- (7)
22 Liverpool striker who joined Real Sociedad in 1989 (4, 8)

Down

1 Gordon Milne became Wigan -------- player-manager (8)
2 Players are tested for them! (5)
3 Avi -----, ex-Liverpool defender (5)
4 Left out from the squad (7)
5 Abbreviated nationality of Bill Shankly (4)
6 Gerry and the ----------, performed "You'll never walk alone" (10)
7 Liverpool striker 1998–99 nicknamed Crocodile (4, 6)
11 Not a good game! (3)
12 Colour of Liverpool home shirt (3)
13 Red Star side not Liverpool though! (8)
14 Four in a year only one in football though! (7)
17 Steve Staunton left Anfield for ----- Park in 1991 (5)
18 ----- Tore Kvarme, 1990s Liverpool defender (5)
20 Weather hazard for postponed match, maybe! (4)

Crossword No. 6

Across

3 Mark ---------, 1980s Liverpool defender (9)
8 The Reds have been involved in penalty shoot---- (4)
9 Non-professional players (8)
10 Bert ------, 1950s/60s Reds goalkeeper (6)
13 Requested a transfer (5)
14 Pre-book a place in the second side (7)
15 Jerzy Dudek hides a blank explosive, apparently (3)
16 Tough guys Jimmy Case and Tommy Smith were! (4, 3)
17 Cup settles a giant-killing shock, apparently (5)
21 Reds German international midfielder who scored the last goal at Wembley before it was redeveloped (6)
22 John Barnes came to Anfield from -------- Road, Watford (8)
23 One more than a hat-trick (4)
24 John ---------, 1950s/60s Reds winger who moved across Stanley Park (9)

Down

1 Facial feature for ex-Reds Graeme Souness (9)
2 Positions for ex-Reds Rush and Fowler (9)
4 Bells start ringing when the Reds are losing in extra-time (5)
5 The Reds keeper has stretched and caught ball (7)
6 ---- White, former Reds chairman (4)
7 Do greedy Reds players conceal a giant, apparently (4)
11 Time for early friendlies (3-6)
12 1992 was Liverpool's --------- year (9)
14 At Brunton Park the Reds had a pacy jog, apparently (3)
15 Suffer football losses (7)
18 The Melia days revealed a topical tune, apparently (5)
19 Phil Neal's nickname (4)
20 1910s Reds wing-half Tom ----foul (4)

1	■	2	■	3	4		5		6		7	
8				■		■		■		■		■
	■		■	■	9							
10						■		■		■		■
	■		■	■		■		■	■	11	■	12
13					■	14						
	■		■	■	15			■	■		■	
16							■	17				
	■		■	■		■	18	■	■		■	
■	19	■	20	■		■	21					
22								■	■		■	
■		■		■		■		■	23			
24									■		■	

Crossword No. 7

Across

1 2000s Czech Republic and Liverpool striker (5, 5)
8 Strikes the goal like Ian Rush did! (7)
9 El – – – – – Diouf, 2000s Liverpool forward (5)
10 Chris – – – –land, 2000s Liverpool goalkeeper (4)
11 Flamengo and Brazil midfielder who starred in 1981 World Club Cup against Liverpool (4)
12 Forename of winning FA Cup Final captain in 1965 (3)
14 Emile – – – – – –, 2000s Liverpool striker (6)
15 Big wins, a taxidemist would be proud (6)
18 Liverpool finished – – – of Division One 1990 (3)
20 0–0 is lacking one! (4)
21 Leave out Liverpool player from Italian side, apparently (4)
23 Alf – – – – –smith, 1960s Liverpool marksman (5)
24 In the 1930s, Liverpool toured the Canary ones (7)
25 Fouls with the torso, perhaps! (4, 6)

Down

1 Young footballer gets better with age, like wine, maybe (7)
2 Fortune for Liverpool mascots (4)
3 Widow of Bill Shankly, who represented her husband during the ceremony to close the Kop as a standing terrace in 1994 (6)
4 David – – – – – – – –, Liverpool manager 1920–23 (8)
5 Kevin Keegan is 17 days – – – – – than Kenny Dalglish (5)
6 Injury-jinxed 1970s Reds striker signed from Sheffield Wednesday (4, 7)
7 Stamina exam, maybe! (7, 4)
13 Steve – – – – – – – –, Liverpool forward 1970–81 (8)
16 Goal droughts for hungry strikers (7)
17 Nationality of 1980s/90s midfielder Jan Molby (6)
19 Liverpool knocked out this Portuguese side 2001 UEFA quarter-finals (5)
22 – – – – Lindsay, full-back signed from Bury 1969 (4)

■	■	1		2		3		4		5		■
6	■		■		■		■		■		■	7
8							■	9				
	■		■		■		■		■		■	
10				■	11				■	12		
	■		■	13	■		■		■	■	■	
14						■	15			16		
	■	■	■		■	17	■		■		■	
18		19	■	20				■	21			
	■		■		■		■	22	■		■	
23					■	24						
	■		■		■		■		■		■	
■	25										■	■

Crossword No. 8

Across

1 Attached to the sole of football boots (5)
4 Sounds correct for 1990s Reds and England centre-half Mark (5)
10 Roy, Liverpool manager and joint manager 1994–1998 (5)
11 National team of 2000s midfielder Igor Biscan (7)
12 Bill Shankly discovered this famous Manchester United player (5, 3)
13 Nice picture for Liverpool classic, apparently (4)
15 No pre-match butterflies for ex-defender William Steele (6)
17 – – – – – – Patterson, Liverpool manager, 1928–36 (6)
19 What a substitute does on the bench (4)
20 Liverpool's is Reds or Pool (8)
23 Jim – – – – – – –, goalkeeper who joined Arsenal in 1962 (7)
24 Frantic match hides prank, apparently (5)
25 – – – – – Hanson, 1930s outside-left not Hitler though! (5)
26 First goal – – – – – the scoring (5)

Down

2 Catch one during Liverpool match training, apparently (5)
3 Relegation would be one for Liverpool (8)
5 Alter football coin for ex-Liverpool boss, Bill Shankly (anag) (4)
6 Jamie Redknapp left Liverpool for Tottenham – – – – – – – (7)
7 There were two in the 1974 FA Charity Shield match against Leeds United (8, 3)
8 Liverpool fans keep cuttings in this type of book (5)
9 Former Liverpool and England goalkeeper (3, 8)
14 Jamie – – – – – – – –, 1990s/2000s injury-jinxed midfielder (8)
16 Ex-Reds defender Mark Lawrenson – – – – – – – through injury 1988 (7)
18 An– – – – – Stadium, the Reds' home (5)
21 Robbie Fowler scored a hat-trick against – – – – – Villa 1998 (5)
22 Part of the foot for back flick! (4)

■	1	2		3		■	4	5		6		■
7	■		■		■	8	■		■		■	9
10					■	11						
	■		■		■		■		■		■	
12								■	13			
	■	■	■		■		■	14	■		■	
15		16				■	17					
	■		■		■	18	■		■	■	■	
19				■	20					21		
	■		■	22	■		■		■		■	
23							■	24				
	■		■		■		■		■		■	
■	25					■	26					■

Crossword No. 9

Across

1 Steven - - - - - - -, home-grown midfielder (7)
7 Number of times Liverpool have won the League Cup (5)
8 US city where in 1946 Liverpool played the - - - - - - - All-Stars (3, 4)
9 Venues such as Anfield and Goodison Park (6)
11 - - - - - Heighway ex-Liverpool forward (5)
13 What a frozen pitch needs to do before becoming playable (4)
14 The last team to defeat Liverpool in front of the standing Kop! (7)
15 Liverpool skit reveals football strips (anag) (4)
16 Player's cup final memento (5)
17 Score draw involving two goals (3, 3)
21 Graeme, Liverpool boss 1991–94 (7)
22 Karl-- - - - - - Riedle, 1990s Reds striker (5)
23 Infringing ex-Liverpool striker Robbie Fowler, perhaps! (7)

Down

2 Blue Liverpudlian! (10)
3 Liverpool manager 1994–98 (3, 5)
4 Titi Camara reportedly was scarce, apparently (4)
5 Brian - - - -, 2000s Republic of Ireland boss (4)
6 - - - - Saunders, ex-Liverpool and Wales striker (4)
9 Escape relegation (5)
10 Ex-Liverpool defender now television football pundit (4, 6)
12 - - - - - Grobbelaar, ex-Liverpool goalkeeper (5)
13 Comfortable home score for Liverpool (5, 3)
18 Everton will wait an eternity, apparently (4)
19 Liverpool once beat Crystal Palace - - - - nil (4)
20 Pool changes to a different sport (anag) (4)

WALK ALONE

Crossword No. 10

Across

1 Chris Kirkland made his against Grimsby Town 2001 (5)
7 Kenny --------, 1912–20 Liverpool and Scotland keeper (8)
8 ----- Geli, scored an own-goal in Reds favour UEFA Cup Final 2001 (5)
10 Liverpool's original nickname (10)
12 Losing captain in 2003 Worthington Cup Final (3, 5)
14 Red or yellow! (4)
16 1960s/70s Liverpool goalkeeper Ray Clemence left for Tottenham Hot ---- (4)
17 Matches for forwards, maybe (8)
20 2000s, Liverpool striker (4, 6)
23 Club crests involve taking breaks, apparently (5)
24 Removing a hooligan from the stadium (8)
25 Birmingham suburb where Liverpool won 1981 League Cup (5)

Down

1 Didi Agathe, though not Hamann! (6)
2 Liverpool have won the ---- Cup three times (4)
3 ---- Litmanen, ex-Liverpool and Finland forward (4)
4 Check your spelling for loan period, apparently (5)
5 It would be a disaster if Liverpool were! (9)
6 Transfer windows are during certain times of the season (6)
9 ----- Milan not Baros though! (5)
11 Scottish club Steve Nicol left to join Liverpool (3, 6)
13 Reverse ten to find the back of it (anag) (3)
15 Not a serious injury (5)
16 ------ Westerveld, former Liverpool and Holland keeper (6)
18 Joe Fagan won 3 cups in his first ------ (6)
19 Tommy -----, "The Anfield Iron" (5)
21 French side El Hadji Diouf signed for Liverpool from 2002 (4)
22 The nickname of Liverpool (4)

1			2		■	3	■	4	■	5	■	6
	■	■		■	7							
8				9	■		■		■		■	
	■	■	10									
	■	11	■		■	■	■		■		■	
12						13		■	14			
■	■		■		■		■	15	■		■	■
16				■	17							18
	■		■	19	■	■	■		■		■	
20						21			22	■	■	
	■		■		■		■	23				
24								■		■	■	
	■		■		■		■	25				

Crossword No. 11

Across

6 Numerical shirt feature for Vladimir Smicer in 2003–04 (6, 6)
8 What defenders concede when they clear the ball into the crowd behind the goal (7)
9 Ring Owen to find Beatles drummer of yesteryear, apparently (5)
10 Chris Lawler played for Liverpool as a full- - - - - (4)
12 1990s/2000s Liverpool striker - - - - - - Fowler (6)
14 Kevin - - - - -, Liverpool-born midfielder who scored Bolton's winner at Anfield in 2002 (5)
15 - - - - - - Whelan, Liverpool midfielder 1979–93 (6)
16 Not a short ball (4)
19 Gerry - - - - -, 1950s/60s Liverpool full-back (5)
21 David Fairclough left Liverpool to play for this Swiss League club (7)
22 Liverpool defender signed from WBA in 1988 (5, 7)

Down

1 Nationality of ex-Liverpool keeper, Brad Friedel (8)
2 When Liverpool equalise they have drawn - - - - - (5)
3 Nationality of former Liverpool defender, Joey Jones (5)
4 No pears for 1910s/20s Liverpool outside-left, Albert (anag) (7)
5 - - - - Michel Ferri, Gerard Houllier's first signing for Liverpool (4)
6 1990s/2000s, Everton, Liverpool and England midfielder (4, 6)
7 General term for Reds players from outside Britain (10)
11 Digit to extend foot's length, apparently (3)
12 - - - Clemence, former Liverpool goalkeeper (3)
13 Anfield's legendary inner sanctum, from where coaches were promoted to manager (4, 4)
14 Crystal Palace's record league defeat was this score against Liverpool (4, 3)
17 Football associations are suited for cards (5)
18 Red and white neckwear for Liverpool fan (5)
20 Anfield - - - -, address of the Reds' stadium (4)

■	■	1	■	2	■	3	■	4	■	5	■	■
6												■
	■		■		■		■		■		■	7
8							■	9				
	■		■		■		■		■	■	■	
10				■	11	■	12			13		
	■		■	14					■		■	
15						■		■	16			
	■	■	■		■	17	■	18	■		■	
19		20			■	21						
	■		■		■		■		■		■	
■	22											
■	■		■		■		■		■		■	■

Crossword No. 12

Across

3 Star sign of Emile Heskey (9)
8 Nickname of team to beat Liverpool in 1988 FA Cup Final (4)
9 Referee or matchday programme (8)
10 St Ivan reveals ex-Reds midfielder Mr Kozma's forename (anag) (6)
13 Howard – – – –, first black player to play for Liverpool (5)
14 Liverpool were founded in the nineteenth – – – – – – – (7)
15 Honorary award for Gerard Houllier, initially (3)
16 When Keegan left, did it make the Liverpool fans hearts grow fonder (7)
17 Bruno – – – – – of AS Roma missed a penalty against Liverpool in 1984 European Cup Final (5)
21 Real Spanish side Steve McManaman played for! (6)
22 1990s, Liverpool midfielder (4, 4)
23 In penalty shoot-out each player must take his – – – – (4)
24 The Liverbird is part of Liverpool's (4, 5)

Down

1 Ex-Reds midfielder Nicky Barmby played under this Leeds United caretaker-manager in 2003–04 (5, 4)
2 Area in Liverpool associated with Ken Dodd and The Diddymen (6, 3)
4 "You'll never walk – – – – –" (5)
5 His room at Anfield is the smallest of three changing rooms (7)
6 Liverpool won the – – – –-Cola Cup 1995 (4)
7 Kemlyn – – – – Stand, of yesteryear Liverpool (4)
11 Liverpool were European Super Cup – – – – – – – – – – 1985 (7-2)
12 Liverpool centre-forward of 1930s/40s/50s (5, 4)
14 Initial award for ex-chairman John Smith prior to receiving his knighthood (3)
15 In 2001 League Cup Final, Martin –'– – – – – – was fouled by Stephane Henchoz to win a penalty for Birmingham (1'6)
18 Certain signs are hidden in womens football, apparently (5)
19 Brian – – – –, 1970s midfielder (4)
20 Liverpool Football – – – – (4)

1	■	2	■	3	4		5		6		7	
8				■		■		■		■		■
	■		■	■	9							
10						■		■		■		■
	■		■	■		■		■	■	11	■	12
13					■	14						
	■		■	■	15			■	■		■	
16							■	17				
	■		■	■		■	18	■	■		■	
■	19	■	20	■		■	21					
22								■	■		■	
■		■		■		■		■	23			
24									■		■	

Crossword No. 13

Across

1 Irish capital for ex-Liverpool forward Steve Heighway (6, 4)
8 Be anxious during penalties, perhaps (7)
9 Star sign of legendary goalscorer Ian Rush (5)
10 Way out at Anfield (4)
11 Uneven match betting prices (4)
12 Gerard Houllier hides an age, apparently (3)
14 European exit can be an expensive mistake, maybe (6)
15 In 1996 Anfield staged an international match involving this foreign side (6)
18 - - - Watson, Liverpool boss 1896–1915 (3)
20 - - - - McQueen, Liverpool boss 1923–28 (4)
21 Over two legs Liverpool beat this Finnish club 9–1 (4)
23 Forename of ex-Liverpool star "Crazy Horse", Mr Hughes (5)
24 Steve Nicol went to coach in this Northern Continent (7)
25 Bayer - - - - - - - - - -, knocked out Liverpool from 2001–02 Champions League (10)

Down

1 Local games like that against Everton (7)
2 Crowd jeers! (4)
3 Roger Hunt played - - - - - --right in old 2–3–5 formation (6)
4 Bill Shankly described Ron Yeats as his - - - - - - - - (8)
5 Bleat about football division (anag) (5)
6 Liverpool reached the semi-final of this cup in 1971 (5-6)
7 Turkish side Graeme Souness managed (11)
13 Ray - - - - - - - -, Liverpool goalkeeping legend (8)
16 Lime Street for Liverpool (7)
17 Forward line for 2000s Liverpool's Heskey and Owen (6)
19 Gordon - - - - -, 1960s Liverpool right half (5)
22 Graeme Souness hides Loch monster, apparently (4)

Crossword No. 13

■	■	1		2		3		4		5		■
6	■		■		■		■		■		■	7
8							■	9				
	■		■		■		■		■		■	
10				■	11				■	12		
	■		■	13	■		■		■	■	■	
14						■	15			16		
	■	■	■		■	17	■		■		■	
18		19	■	20				■	21			
	■		■		■		■	22	■		■	
23					■	24						
	■		■		■		■		■		■	
■	25										■	■

Crossword No. 14

Across

1 Jan -----, 1980s/90s Reds midfielder (5)
4 Nationality of John Toshack (5)
10 ----- Hunt, Liverpool goalscoring legend (5)
11 Ronny Rosenthal's nationality (7)
12 I end limb to find the referee Tommy Smith kicked after Inter Milan beat Reds in 1965 European Cup semi-final (anag) (8)
13 Even the hottest of "Supersubs", such as David Fairclough, had to ----up (4)
15 The Terrors reveal defensive mistakes, apparently (6)
17 Club that knocked Liverpool out of the 2002–03 UEFA Cup (6)
19 Red stocking for Liverpool, not a pair though! (4)
20 Position for 2000s Vegard Heggem (8)
23 Nationality of Liverpool's 1984 European Cup final opponents (7)
24 What Danny Murphy keeps when taking penalties (5)
25 ----- Kelly, equalised for Arsenal against the Reds 1971 FA Cup Final (5)
26 Larry -----, 1960s/70s Liverpool centre-half (5)

Down

2 This, in Liverpool, is a vital part of the body (5)
3 Crush --------, safety structures once found in the Kop (8)
5 Country Steve Staunton played for (short) (4)
6 Paul -------, 1990s attacking midfielder (7)
7 League which Liverpool has graced since 1992 (11)
8 Four or six Romans could go into 199 for this type of reception for cup winners! (5)
9 1990s Liverpool winger, though not ex-US president! (5, 6)
14 Liverpool beat Tottenham Hotspur by this score 1978 (5, 3)
16 ------- Money, 1980s Liverpool defender (7)
18 ----- Dalglish, former Liverpool legend (5)
21 When the Reds play at Pride Park is it this type of match? (5)
22 ---- Hamann, 2000s Liverpool (short) (4)

Crossword No. 15

Across

1 Steve – – – – – – –, ex-Liverpool player went on to manage Swindon Town (7)
7 – – – – – Redknapp, former Liverpool and England midfielder (5)
8 Hyped up and rejected Liverpool players have, perhaps! (7)
9 Kevin – – – – – –, former Liverpool and England striker (6)
11 Aggregates through which one gets attendances, apparently (5)
13 – – – – Johnson, scored 14 goals in 1922–23 title season (4)
14 Mediocre performance, perhaps! (7)
15 Oakfield or Walton Breck – – – – Stand was replaced by the Spion Kop in 1905–06 (4)
16 Nickname of ex-Reds striker Dean Saunders (5)
17 – – – – – – Kay, Liverpool boss 1936–51 (6)
21 Football analysts like Mark Lawrenson and Alan Hansen (7)
22 Jerzy – – – – –, 2000s Reds goalkeeper (5)
23 – – – – – – – Sinama Pongolle, 2000s Liverpool striker (7)

Down

2 Gerry Byrne played the 1965 FA Cup Final with a broken – – – – – – – – – – (10)
3 Pegguy – – – – – – – –, 2000s Liverpool goalkeeper signed from Leicester (8)
4 Michael – – – –, 1990s/2000s striker (4)
5 Delayed kick-off tells a tale (anag) (4)
6 Steven Gerrard is marking royalty, apparently (4)
9 Make Babb a Turkish sandwich, apparently (5)
10 Former Red Mike Marsh finished his career at – – – – – – – – – – Stanley (10)
12 Don – – – – –, managed Liverpool's opponents in the 1965 FA Cup Final (5)
13 Position for 2000s Sami Hyypia (8)
18 Penalty-taking responsibility at Anfield is on us, apparently (4)
19 – – – – Hysen, 1980s/90s Swedish centre-back (4)
20 Remove four letters from Houllier to find City side (4)

LIVERPOOL
FOOTBALL CLUB

Crossword No. 16

Across

1 - - - - - Hoddle, famously said, "Michael Owen is not a natural goalscorer" (5)
7 Bill Shankly unsuccessfully tried to sign this Scottish striker (5, 3)
8 George - - - - -, Reds first Scottish international (5)
10 Would the Moscow or Leipzig team train at Lime Street station? Sounds like it! (10)
12 Part swap like that between Dicks and Burrows (8)
14 Former Reds right-half Ted Savage shows eras, apparently (4)
16 Forename of footballer Whelan but not ex-Reds Ronnie though! (4)
17 Skippers like Emlyn Hughes and Steven Gerrard (8)
20 Numerical term for ex-Reds centre-half, Ron Yeats (6, 4)
23 - - - - - Blenkinsop, 1930s Reds and England full-back in short (5)
24 Striker like 2000s Red Milan Baros (8)
25 Arthur - - - - -, music-hall comedian who attended Anfield in the good old Shankly days! (5)

Down

1 Forename of former Reds boss, Mr Souness (6)
2 Phil - - - -, 1970s/80s England defender (4)
3 Froze round 32°F at Anfield in centigrade apparently! (4)
4 Steve - - - - -, former Reds defender nicknamed "Chico" (5)
5 The nickname of ex-Reds keeper Tommy Lawrence (6, 3)
6 Proprietors like Liverpool's John Houlding! (6)
9 Kevin - - - - -, Bolton midfielder once on Liverpool's books (5)
11 Terry - - - - - - - - -, midfielder, signed from Newcastle (9)
13 Liverpool goalmouth hides Indian region, apparently (3)
15 - - - - - McManaman, who won a Champions League medal after leaving Anfield (5)
16 1970s Liverpool and Wales striker John Toshack arrived at Anfield from - - - - - - Park (6)
18 Kevin - - - - - -, midfielder who played one full game for the Reds but hundreds for Everton (6)
19 - - - - - Saul, played 83 games as Liverpool full-back (5)
21 No money involved in Jamie Redknapp transfer (4)
22 You can argue Rosenthal hid a Greek God, apparently (4)

Crossword No. 17

Across

6 Midfielder who made his debut in 1981 (6, 6)
8 Thomas -------, 1950s goalkeeper who was never older (7)
9 Alter harps for an acute shooter (anag) (5)
10 Ex-Liverpool defender Avi Cohen signed from Maccabi Tel ---- (4)
12 Distributor of the ball! (6)
14 A free role at Blackburn? (5)
15 Igor ------, versatile 2000s Liverpool player (6)
16 Ex-Liverpool striker John ----es went on to manage Celtic (4)
19 Chris Lawler played -----back for Liverpool (5)
21 -- ----- Diouf, 2000s Liverpool and Senegal forward (2, 5)
22 The year of Liverpool's first Football League and UEFA Cup Double, nineteen ------------ (7-5)

Down

1 Problems for ex-Reds midfielder Jamie Redknapp amongst others (8)
2 Star sign of Markus Babbel (5)
3 A draw shows a Liverpool player honour (anag) (5)
4 Belgrade team not Liverpool celebrity though! (3, 4)
5 Whilst boss of Galatasaray Graeme Souness enjoyed a celebration, apparently (4)
6 Full-back at Anfield for over twenty years, 1930s/40s/50s (3, 7)
7 Young football trainee (10)
11 --- Hutchison, 1990s Scottish international signed from Hartlepool (3)
12 Ex-Liverpool forward Peter Beardsley hides teachers favourite, apparently (3)
13 -------- Liege, Belgian opponents in 1965–66 European Cup Winners Cup (8)
14 Noisy items for Liverpool fans of yesteryear (7)
17 ----- Burkinshaw, only ex-Red player to manage against Liverpool in a cup final (5)
18 Colour associated with Liverpool shirt collar rims (5)
20 ---- Hysen, 1980s/90s Liverpool and Sweden defender (4)

LIVERPOOL
FOOTBALL CLUB

Crossword No. 18

Across

3 Steve ---------, 1990s midfielder (9)
8 Alter lace for ex left-back Lindsay (anag) (4)
9 Steve --------, 1970s/80s Reds forward (8)
10 Liverpool have been ------ champions a record 18 times (6)
13 A match decided over 120 minutes is decided ----- extra time (5)
14 Paul -------, 1992 £2.3 million signing from Tottenham (7)
15 --- Evans, Liverpool FC manager 1994–98 (3)
16 ------- Wright, defender sold to Sunderland in 2002 (7)
17 Not well enough for match (5)
21 Not offside (6)
22 No tickets left for these capacity crowd games (4, 4)
23 ---- Dundee, ex-Reds who joined Vfb Stuttgart 1999 (4)
24 Alan Hansen likes to comment on these types of player (9)

Down

1 Joined Liverpool FC from Luton Town FC 1984 (4, 5)
2 The Reds won the 1984 European Cup Final 4–2 on --------- (9)
4 Avi -----, left-back signed by Bob Paisley (5)
5 Football skill (7)
6 A Chelsea fixture makes the Reds sore, apparently (4)
7 ---- A'Court, 1950s Reds forward (4)
11 Football intervals (4-5)
12 Reds defender Bjorn Tore Kvarme signed for this French side 1999 (2, 7)
14 Male offspring for 1970s/80s Reds striker David Johnson, apparently (3)
15 Come back off the bar! (7)
18 A cup-final runner-up (5)
19 Tranmere were the only club John Aldridge managed, apparently (4)
20 Shirt colour of Reds FA Cup opponents 1986 (4)

Crossword No. 19

Across

1 1990s Liverpool and England international defender (4, 6)
8 Liverpool's FA Cup Final opponents 2001 (7)
9 - - - - - Carragher, 2000s Liverpool and England defender (5)
10 Time for midday kick-off at Anfield (4)
11 Number of times Liverpool won the European Cup (4)
12 Initially Liverpool supporters are depressed when they lose (3)
14 - - - - - - Dynamo, assisted with fund raising after Hillsborough disaster (6)
15 Nationality of 2000s defender/midfielder Christian Ziege (6)
18 - - - Jones, 1990s Liverpool defender (short) (3)
20 Phil - - - -, defender who went on to manage Coventry City (4)
21 A calm striker provides money for the poor and needy, apparently (4)
23 Bingo term when Anfield is full (5)
24 Red carded (4, 3)
25 Ex-Liverpool striker Stan Collymore was signed from this Forest side (10)

Down

1 Lucky charms may lead teams on to the pitch! (7)
2 Unbeaten jogs (4)
3 Charlie - - - - - -, wing-half and coach at Liverpool, 1897–1936 (6)
4 Cause of Liverpool players to miss game (8)
5 Games at Anfield, not aways! (5)
6 Liverpool midfielder signed from Crewe Alexandra 1997 (5, 6)
7 Dismissals of more than one player (7, 4)
13 Michael Owen is the - - - - - - - - player to score for Liverpool (8)
16 - - - - - - - McVean scored Liverpool's first-ever Football League goal (7)
17 Alan - - - - - -, ex-Liverpool and Scotland defender (6)
19 - - - - - Cheyrou, 2000s Liverpool midfielder (5)
22 In Cheyrou you will find a measurement, apparently (4)

Crossword No. 20

Across

1 Willie Stevenson left Liverpool for this City club in 1968 (5)
4 Player bid, perhaps! (5)
10 Foreign player from Jupiter, maybe! (5)
11 Whistle-blower who is in control (7)
12 Michael Owen was a -------- when he made his debut (8)
13 Patrice ----, goalkeeper who made his Liverpool debut against Chelsea in January 2004 (4)
15 Tommy Lawrence's shirt ------ was one! (6)
17 Did ex-Reds Geoff Strong have large upper arm muscles (6)
19 Footballer of the ---- 1976 was Kevin Keegan (4)
20 Teams can come to Anfield and not play positive football (8)
23 Our blue neighbours! (7)
24 Not a sitting feature at Anfield (5)
25 Former currency for Gerard Houllier (5)
26 Takes part in match! (5)

Down

2 Number of times Liverpool have been World Club runners-up (5)
3 1990s Liverpool chairman Noel White's counterpart at Chelsea was --- ----- (3, 5)
5 World football organisation (4)
6 Are the French on their way to Anfield (2, 5)
7 TV football commentator (6, 5)
8 Star sign of Tommy Smith (5)
9 Ex-Liverpool and Everton midfielder (5, 6)
14 Cypriot club Apoel --------, played the Reds in 1988–89 (8)
16 Jason -------, former Liverpool and Republic of Ireland international (7)
18 Graeme answers that he intends to be rich, apparently (5)
21 Ian Rush first left Liverpool to play in this country (5)
22 ---- Collymore, 1990s Liverpool striker (4)

■	1	2		3		■	4	5		6		■
7	■		■		■	8	■		■		■	9
10					■	11						
	■		■		■		■		■		■	
12								■	13			
	■	■	■		■		■	14	■		■	
15		16				■	17					
	■		■		■	18	■		■	■	■	
19				■	20					21		
	■		■	22	■		■		■		■	
23							■	24				
	■		■		■		■		■		■	
■	25					■	26					■

Crossword No. 21

Across

1 Did Reds player Ian Ross appear at AC Milan stadium (anag) (3, 4)
7 Liverpool shows match betting coupon, apparently (5)
8 Reds striker David Fairclough was always on call! (5, 2)
9 Nears a stadium like Anfield and Goodison Park (anag) (6)
11 Have fun watching Liverpool win (5)
13 - - - - Hyypia, 1990s/2000s Reds defender (4)
14 - - - - - - - Sinama Pongolle, 2000s Reds forward (7)
15 This type of goal difference is normally the sign of a winning team (4)
16 Rises to head the ball and plenty at Aintree (5)
17 Cousin of England star Chris, Alan played 22 times for the Reds in the 1970s (6)
21 Famous Liverpool Fab Four but not the Reds' defence! (7)
22 Paul - - - - -, 1980s Liverpool forward made debut against Everton (5)
23 Liverpool FC, - - - - - - - 1892 (7)

Down

2 *13 down* played for both Liverpool and this club twice (5, 5)
3 Leaving parties, but not really red cards (4-4)
4 Shrubs conceal massages on the Reds treatment table, apparently (4)
5 Jim Furnell arrived at Anfield from Turf - - - - (4)
6 Strategy for Liverpool game (4)
9 *21 across* recorded on this Road, but not at Cambridge United's Stadium (5)
10 Exciting game can create an electric feeling at Anfield (10)
12 Will avid Liverpool FC fan Ricky Tomlinson welcome Toffeeman Joe to be a member of his famous TV *Family*? (5)
13 Steve - - - - - - - -, 1980s/90s/2000s Liverpool and Ireland defender (8)
18 A goalless one is often called a "bore - - - -" (4)
19 Fixture - - - - (4)
20 What Michael Owen is and another one might be, apparently (4)

1	2		3		4		■	5	■	6	■	■
■		■		■		■	7					■
8							■		■		■	■
■		■		■		■	9				10	
11					■	■		■	■	■		■
■		■		■	12	■		■	13			
■		■	14							■		■
15				■		■		■		■		■
■		■	■	■		■	■	16				
17		18		19		■	20	■		■		■
■	■		■		■	21						
■	22					■		■		■		■
■	■		■		■	23						

Crossword No. 22

Across

1 1950s/60s/70s, Reds Ian Callaghan was a ----- winger (5)
7 Bill Shankly brought a winning one to Anfield in the 1960s (8)
8 Heads or ----- was called in the Reds 1965 European Cup tie (5)
10 1960s/70s, Reds defender signed from Bristol Rovers (5, 5)
12 Chant heard, especially in the 1960s/70s, when Liverpool were winning comfortably (4, 4)
14 David ----clough, was a "Supersub" for the Reds (4)
16 Half or full at Anfield (4)
17 Indirect or direct (4, 4)
20 County League the Reds once played in (10)
23 The nickname of ex-Reds forward, Ian St John (5)
24 Type of transfer swap, maybe! (8)
25 First name of Liverpool goalscorer in 1971 and 1974 FA Cup finals (5)

Down

1 Ex-Reds Roy Evans decided to ------ when aged 25 (6)
2 Brian ----, midfielder signed from Manchester University (4)
3 Shining Liverpool celebrity (4)
4 ----- Liddell, 1930s/40s/50s/60s Reds legend (5)
5 At his peak Ian Rush was such a choice (9)
6 Captain like Emlyn Hughes, perhaps! (6)
9 Dave's stopped great shots (anag) (5)
11 The Reds beat them 8–0 1967–68 Inter-Cities Fairs cup tie (1,1,1, 6)
13 --- John Smith announced that Bill Shankly was retiring (3)
15 Crowd boos from the Kop, perhaps! (5)
16 2000s, Reds player Anthony Le ------ (6)
18 Brian ------, ex-Reds defender is the player to put on at half-time (6)
19 Healthy meal for lads a bit after training, perhaps! (anag) (5)
21 The Reds' Steve Heighway was never low say! (4)
22 Direction of Lancashire Road to Old Trafford from Anfield Road (4)

1			2		■	3	■	4	■	5	■	6
	■	■		■	7							
8				9	■		■		■		■	
	■	■	10									
	■	11	■		■	■	■		■		■	
12						13		■	14			
■	■		■		■		■	15	■		■	■
16				■	17							18
	■		■	19	■	■	■		■		■	
20						21			22	■	■	
	■		■		■		■	23				
24								■		■	■	
	■		■		■		■	25				

Crossword No. 23

Across

6 1980s/90s, Reds defender signed from Sunderland (5, 7)
8 Reuben – – – – – – –, former Reds scout (7)
9 Type of play but not football at Anfield (5)
10 – – – – Xavier, 2000s Reds defender, formerly with Everton (4)
12 Chris – – – – – –, 1950s/60s Reds and England international (6)
14 The Reds golfing term for Leicester City side in the 1960s (5)
15 Robs a goal at Anfield (6)
16 Goal – – – –, part of the woodwork (4)
19 Alun – – – – –, 1960s/70s Reds forward (5)
21 Billy – – – – – – –, long serving Liverpool forward (7)
22 Needed for non-English speaking players at Anfield (12)

Down

1 John Aldridge managed this club 1996–2001 (8)
2 Glen – – – – –, ex-Sweden and Reds defender (5)
3 – – – – – Burkinshaw, ex-Reds player who managed Spurs (5)
4 Alec – – – – – – – –, Reds 1960s/70s defender (7)
5 The Reds have won the Coca-– – – – Cup amongst many others! (4)
6 Ex-Reds boss has a gateway named after him at Anfield (3, 7)
7 Perms were the favourite type amongst 1970s Reds team (10)
11 Costly player reveals a variety of lettuce, apparently (3)
12 Former Reds Jim Beglin broke his against Everton (3)
13 Boots' laces have to be this before they can be removed (8)
14 Ex-Reds player Jimmy Case kicked the ball with power (7)
17 Liverpool rejects are seen as this in many fans' eyes (5)
18 Injury time can be – – – – – on (5)
20 John – – – – Riise, 2000s defender signed from Monaco (4)

■	■	1	■	2	■	3	■	4	■	5	■	■
6												■
	■		■		■		■		■		■	7
8							■	9				
	■		■		■		■		■	■	■	
10				■	11	■	12			13		
	■		■	14					■		■	
15						■		■	16			
	■	■	■		■	17	■	18	■		■	
19		20			■	21						
	■		■		■		■		■		■	
■	22											
■	■		■		■		■		■		■	■

Across

3 Terry ---------, assisted Kevin Keegan on the pitch at Anfield and off it at Newcastle (9)
8 Tommy Smith was known as "The Anfield ----" (4)
9 Selecting new Reds boss by votes, apparently (8)
10 Liverpool's ------ team was formed in 1989 (6)
13 ----- Brown, Everton player who scored an own-goal 1969–70 derby match (5)
14 Stadium where Liverpool played Barcelona in *19 down* 2001 semi-final (3, 4)
15 Ex-Reds Dominic Matteo nears age, apparently (3)
16 Republic country of birth for 1960s/70s forward, Steve Heighway (7)
17 Happy crowd noise from the Kop (5)
21 Liverpool and Everton are! (6)
22 Show Liverpool matches on TV (8)
23 Ex-Reds keeper David James was there to (4)
24 Forenames of 1990s/2000s Reds forward, Mr Riedle (4-5)

Down

1 Gary ---------, former Reds defender (9)
2 Managed Everton the same time as Bob Paisley was managing Liverpool (6, 3)
4 Part of the body for Michael Owen's birthplace Chester, apparently (5)
5 FA Cup runners-up when Liverpool completed championship and FA Cup double (7)
6 Team reveals friend (anag) (4)
7 ---- Hateley, 1960s Reds forward (4)
11 One of those who film the action at Anfield for live television (9)
12 Keegan competed with others on TV's "Superstars" (9)
14 Ex-Reds boss Don Welsh partly used his head (anag) (3)
15 Ask about a player to join Anfield, perhaps! (7)
18 Usual jersey colour for 1950s/60s/70s Liverpool goalkeepers (5)
19 Liverpool won the ---- Cup 2001 (4)
20 Alter Pele for orange skin (anag) (4)

1	■	2	■	3	4		5		6		7	
8				■		■		■		■		■
	■		■	■	9							
10						■		■		■		■
	■		■	■		■		■	■	11	■	12
13					■	14						
	■		■	■	15			■	■		■	
16							■	17				
	■		■	■		■	18	■	■		■	
■	19	■	20	■		■	21					
22								■	■		■	
■		■		■		■		■	23			
24									■		■	

Crossword No. 25

Across

1 Staunch fans (10)
8 Ex-Reds Tony Hateley was - - - - - - - to footballer Mark (7)
9 The Mersey is to Liverpool as the Trent is to Nottingham (5)
10 - - - - Friedel, ex-Reds keeper (4)
11 Graeme Souness managed Turkish side - - - -tasaray (4)
12 - - - Longworth, briefly, was the first Liverpool player to captain England (3)
14 David -'- - - - -, played alongside ex-Reds Mark Lawrenson for Republic of Ireland (1'5)
15 Joe - - - - - -, ex-Evertonian who captained Arsenal in 1950 FA Cup final against the Reds (6)
18 Player on the bench, briefly (3)
20 Lame player may need a dinner (anag) (4)
21 Liverpool beat Everton in the FA Cup - - - - -final 1950 (4)
23 Subs did not exist in the golden days, apparently (5)
24 Player on stand-by, though not a substitute! (7)
25 Previous name of Centenary stand (6, 4)

Down

1 Rescue a point at Anfield (7)
2 Part of goalpost alters to kitchen items (anag) (4)
3 Ex-Reds boss David Ashworth went on to manage this Athletic side (6)
4 The Kop was a famous - - - - - - - - area (8)
5 Don - - - - -, ex-England manager, who was losing boss in the 1965 FA Cup final (5)
6 Turkish side the Reds beat 3–0 at Anfield in 1976–77 (11)
7 First ever Reds foreign player (6, 5)
13 Football hooligan can end up with a - - - - - - - - record (8)
16 Chanted when the Reds scored (7)
17 Lean spell for Liverpool strikers, maybe! (6)
19 Attached to Liverpool shirt (5)
22 A Liverpool coin was issued by this petrol company as part of their FA Cup Centenary collection in 1972 (4)

■	■	1		2		3		4		5		■
6	■		■		■		■		■		■	7
8							■	9				
	■		■		■		■		■		■	
10				■	11				■	12		
	■		■	13	■		■		■	■	■	
14						■	15			16		
	■	■	■		■	17	■		■		■	
18		19	■	20				■	21			
	■		■		■		■	22	■		■	
23					■	24						
	■		■		■		■		■		■	
■	25										■	■

Crossword No. 26

Across

1 Liverpool's shirt colour in 1977 FA Cup Final (5)
4 Midfielder/defender Mike -----, left Liverpool for West Ham and later played for Galatasaray (5)
10 "Crazy -----" nickname of ex-Reds Emlyn Hughes (5)
11 Non-professional player (7)
12 Jari --------, former Reds forward signed from Barcelona (8)
13 Liver ----, part of Reds shirt emblem (4)
15 ------ Leonhardsen, 1990s/2000s Reds and Norway midfielder (6)
17 ------ Riley, 1920s/30s/40s Reds goalkeeper (6)
19 Queens Park Rangers boss phoned Liverpool boss, apparently (4)
20 Forenames of 2000s Norwegian international defender (4, 4)
23 Sounds like 1950s/60s utility player Geoff Strong must have had them (7)
24 ----- Kippe, giant 1990s/2000s defender (5)
25 Tommy Smith has health problems with these leg joints (5)
26 Nationality of striker John Aldridge (5)

Down

2 Geoff -----, England 1966 teammate of Reds forward, Roger Hunt (5)
3 Was Ian St John in this 1960s TV series (3, 5)
5 The Reds are playing but not at Anfield (4)
6 Nationality of coach who led England to 2002 World Cup finals (7)
7 1960s/70s, Reds forward (4, 7)
8 Creature found at Craven Cottage not the Liver, apparently (5)
9 American, ex-Reds, keeper who starred in 2002 World Cup (4, 7)
14 Refs rant at moves, such as John Barnes to Liverpool for £900,000 (anag) (8)
16 Barry -------, 1980s/90s Red who became a TV football pundit (7)
18 Capacity crowd for a full ----- at Anfield (5)
21 Dressing spaces for players to get changed (5)
22 Steve McMahon was not a Red player at Goodison Park (4)

Crossword No. 27

Across

1 When training it appears the Reds are getting wet (7)
7 National side Dean Saunders played for (5)
8 Formal forename for the legendary Mr Dalglish (7)
9 Sounds like Florent - - - - - - Pongolle could have been seen at a picture house (6)
11 Ways out at Anfield (5)
13 Solo jogs (4)
14 - - - - - - - Diouf, 2000s Reds striker (2, 5)
15 2000s Reds defender Steve Finnan hides Irish club - - - - Harps, apparently (4)
16 Not the upper terrace at Anfield (5)
17 Djimi - - - - - -, 2000s Liverpool defender (6)
21 In nineteen - - - - - - - -four Liverpool won FA Cup for the second time (7)
22 "You'll - - - - - Walk Alone" at Anfield (5)
23 List stating forthcoming games at Anfield (7)

Down

2 2000s Liverpool defender (4, 6)
3 The age Emile Heskey became on 11 January, 1998 (8)
4 Alter nest for goalkeeping mesh (4)
5 - - - - Hyypia, Liverpool defender (4)
6 Liverpool were - - - - Cup winners 2001 (4)
9 - - - - - Louis II, site of Liverpool's 2001 Super Cup success (5)
10 - - - - - - - - - - United lost to Liverpool in the 2003 Worthington Cup final (10)
12 Hears rumours that Anfield may be with Goodison Park ground (anag) (5)
13 - - - - - - - - Song, Liverpool's first Cameroon defender (8)
18 - - - - Lindsay, ex-Liverpool defender (4)
19 Regretted the rude remark to the referee (anag) (4)
20 - - - -circle is a football pitch feature (4)

1	2		3		4		■	5	■	6	■	■
■		■		■		■	7					■
8							■		■		■	■
■		■		■		■	9				10	
11					■	■		■	■	■		■
■		■		■	12	■		■	13			
■		■	14							■		■
15				■		■		■		■		■
■		■	■	■		■	■	16				
17		18		19		■	20	■		■		■
■	■		■		■	21						
■	22					■		■		■		■
■	■		■		■	23						

Crossword No. 28

Across

1 3pm is an - - - - -noon kick-off (5)
7 In 1940–41 Liverpool travelled to Spotland to play this club in the North Regional League (8)
8 Reds chose depot when going for a different formation (anag) (5)
10 Tabloids or broadsheets (10)
12 The result of the 1989 FA Cup final, the Hillsborough Tribute Final (5, 3)
14 Sporting event involving two teams, maybe pheasant and quail (4)
16 Rigobert - - - -, Cameroon international defender (4)
17 Ronny Rosenthal arrived at Liverpool from - - - - - - - - Liège (8)
20 Kenny Dalglish became the first Scottish international to win - - - - - - - - - - caps (3, 7)
23 Sharp nickname of ex-Reds defender, Neil Ruddock (5)
24 John Toshack managed Real - - - - - - - - (8)
25 Jimmy - - - - -, former Reds forward (5)

Down

1 Alan -'- - - - -, 1950s/60s Reds winger who lost his place to Peter Thompson (1'5)
2 Eight is not an odd score (4)
3 - - - -' Pen, old enclosure at Anfield which separated the men from them (4)
4 Dishonest player (5)
5 He will take shots at Anfield to be seen in *10 across* (9)
6 A player in the Liverpool second team could be called this (6)
9 - - - - - Dougan played for Wolves whilst Ian St John was a Red (5)
11 - - - - - - - - - Totti, Roma striker kept quiet by Liverpool defence in 2001–02 Champions League (9)
13 See *16 down* for a sharp mind (3)
15 Not an overarm throw for Liverpool goalkeepers (5)
16 (and *13 down*) The Liverpool sense of humour is a much-admired trait (6, 3)
18 Alou - - - - - -, 2000s midfielder signed by Liverpool from Bayern Munich, but who never played for the first team(6)
19 Jerzy - - - - -, 2000s Polish goalkeeper at Anfield (5)
21 Level result (4)
22 Ian Rush's - - - - of birth is 20 October 1961 (4)

Crossword No. 29

Across

6 Liverpool were losing FA – – —– – – – – – – – – at Wembley, 1977 (3, 9)
8 Writing instruments used for bookings, perhaps! (7)
9 World Cup Final strike partner of Roger Hunt, Geoff – – – – – (5)
10 – – – – Biscan, versatile 2000s Reds player (4)
12 – – – – – – Bennett, 1950s/60s/70s Reds coach (6)
14 On arrival an Everton fan is hiding, apparently (5)
15 No lens shows the club ex-Reds boss Joe Fagan played for (anag) (6)
16 – – – – Diarra, 2000s Reds defender spent a year on-loan with Le Havre (4)
19 John Arne – – – – –, 2000s Norwegian born Reds defender (5)
21 Ray Kennedy was signed from this club in 1974 (7)
22 1966 World Cup final goalscorer, teammate of *9 across*, but not Roger Hunt (6, 6)

Down

1 Vacant target (4, 4)
2 – – – – – Dean, presented Kevin Keegan with Footballer of the Year award 1976 (5)
3 1960s/70s, legendary Reds forward – – – – – John (3, 2)
4 – – – – – – – Thomas, 1990s Reds midfielder (7)
5 Wallacetown, – – – –lingshire, birthplace of 1890s/1900s legend Alex Raisbeck (4)
6 In March and May 2001, Liverpool were twice – – – – – – – – – – in Cardiff (3-7)
7 Legendary Wolves player then manager recruited during war years at Anfield (4, 6)
11 Gain three points (3)
12 – – – Clemence, 1960s/70s/80s Liverpool & England keeper (3)
13 Players are encouraged to eat a well-– – – – – – – – diet (8)
14 – – – – – – – Carlos, teammate of Steve McManaman when at Real Madrid (7)
17 – – – – – Murphy, 1990s/2000s Reds midfielder (5)
18 Speed is an invaluable one to Michael Owen (5)
20 – – – – Alonso, Alaves player who scored against Reds in the 2001 UEFA Cup final (4)

Crossword No. 30

Across

3 League and Super Cup winners 1986 (9)
8 Reach every Reds player, apparently (4)
9 Garment worn by Reds boss on cold Anfield nights (8)
10 Cottage where ex-Reds Kevin Keegan spent time as manager (6)
13 In theatrical terms Anfield is Liverpool's platform (5)
14 The club nickname of Everton (7)
15 – – – Yeats, legendary 1960s/70s Reds centre-half (3)
16 Material for old style football (7)
17 – – – – – Traore, 2000s Reds defender (5)
21 No place in football for these views (6)
22 1989 FA Cup Final Liverpool beat Everton by this score aet (5, 3)
23 Train in wet weather, apparently (4)
24 Boss of *1 down* in 1974 FA Cup final (3, 6)

Down

1 Liverpool's opponents in the 1974 FA Cup Final (9)
2 Steve – – – – – – – – –, left Liverpool for Real Madrid then Manchester City (9)
4 Football legends like Bill Shankly (5)
5 1990s winger Mark Walters' second name might have been more popular elsewhere on Merseyside (7)
6 Select player (4)
7 Nickname of striker Ian Rush (4)
11 Stage in cup competitions when just four teams remain (4-5)
12 Phil Thompson 2000s Reds – – – – – – – – – manager (9)
14 Bjorn Tore Kvarme hides high hill, apparently (3)
15 Liverpool lost home and away to – – – – – – – Belgrade 1973 (3, 4)
18 Fractured a goalscoring record, maybe! (5)
19 – – – – Kelly tossed a coin for the signature of Albert Stubbins and lost (4)
20 Goal netting (4)

LIVERPOOL
FOOTBALL CLUB

WALK ALONE

Crossword No. 31

Across

1 Joined Liverpool from across Stanley Park in summer 2000 (4, 6)
8 Football experts like Lawrenson & Hansen (7)
9 Remove all-red Liverpool kit, maybe! (5)
10 Left flank for ex-Reds Steve Heighway (4)
11 Kevin Keegan was 1976 Football of the – – – – (4)
12 She might bring legal action if a deal seems fraudulent (3)
14 Scottish club Kenny Dalglish arrived from (6)
15 Arsène – – – – – –, Houllier's counterpart in 2001 FA Cup final (6)
18 Cup match (3)
20 Finnish club, – – – – Pallooseura, beaten 10–1 at Anfield in October 1980 (4)
21 Tommy Smith was known as The Anfield – – – – (4)
23 Noel – – – – –, 2000s Liverpool FC chairman (5)
24 Standing area for fans (7)
25 Sander – – – – – – – – – –, ex-Liverpool FC goalkeeper (10)

Down

1 Liverpool FC beat Crystal Palace – – – – – – – 1989 (4, 3)
2 Icon is flipped to commence match (anag) (4)
3 Graeme Souness did this figuratively in midfield in the 1970s/80s and officially from the dugout in the 1990s (6)
4 Second team players (8)
5 Milan – – – – –, 2000s Liverpool and Czech Republic forward (5)
6 David Johnson signed for Liverpool from this East Anglian club in 1976 (7, 4)
7 Tommy Lawrence made 390 – – – – – – – – – – – for the Reds (11)
13 – – – – – – – – Song, 1990s/2000s defender and Cameroon international (8)
16 Steven – – – – – – –, 1990s/2000s Reds midfielder (7)
17 Bert – – – – – –, 1950s/60s Scottish-born goalkeeper (6)
19 – – – – – Heskey, 2000s Liverpool and England striker (5)
22 – – – –-kick (4)

Crossword No. 32

Across

1 Nationality of 2000s Reds defender, Stephane Henchoz (5)
4 Smashes and - - - - -, the sort of raids when Liverpool snatch the points (5)
10 Anfield is to Liverpool as - - - - - Park is to Derby County (5)
11 Ze - - - - - - -, defender who played for Bayer Leverkusen against Liverpool in 2002 Champions League (7)
12 Removing streaker from the ground, perhaps! (8)
13 Frugal Anelka hides celebration, apparently (4)
15 Gerard Houllier managed the Reds when Bobby - - - - - - managed the Magpies (6)
17 Sounds like one complained about Bordeaux (6)
19 Shirt number for Ian St John (4)
20 - - - - - - - - Dortmund, beat Liverpool in 1966 Cup-winners Cup final (8)
23 Not an afternoon kick-off at Anfield (7)
24 Harry Kewell hides a place in Surrey, apparently (5)
25 Bristol even pinched Larry Lloyd, apparently (5)
26 County where 1980s Reds midfielder Ronnie Whelan managed the Shrimpers (5)

Down

2 Dick - - - - -, 1950s/60s Liverpool centre-half (5)
3 Bill Shankly invented this training technique (8)
5 1990s Reds defender Mr Jones steals a goal say (4)
6 Fantastic buy, such as Kenny Dalglish for £300,000! (7)
7 Alan Kennedy ex-Reds defender made 359 - - - - - - - - - - - for Liverpool (11)
8 Ex-Reds Kenny Dalglish played up - - - - - (5)
9 1970s/80s, Liverpool born Reds forward (6, 5)
14 Callers from the Liverpool touchline (8)
16 Reuben - - - - - - -, on the Reds coaching staff, 1950s/60s (7)
18 - - - - - -tackling defender, how Anfield hero Tommy Smith was often described (5)
21 Nationality of ex-Reds defender, Glen Hysen (short) (5)
22 - - - - Shankly, managed first two Liverpool FA Cup-winning sides (4)

Crossword No. 33

Across

1 Prolific goal - - - - - - - Roger Hunt and Ian Rush (7)
7 Liverpool's coach driver is found in Mersey, apparently (5)
8 Taking part in game (7)
9 - - - - - - Wadsworth, 1910s/20s Reds defender (6)
11 Kevin - - - - -, 1940s/50s Liverpool inside forward (5)
13 Ned - - - -, ex-Reds and Scotland goalkeeper (4)
14 "Supersub" Fairclough joined this Swiss League club (7)
15 - - - -en goal, how the 2001 UEFA Cup Final was decided (4)
16 Surname of 2000s Reds keeper, rival of Chris Kirkland (5)
17 Football outcome (6)
21 - - - - - - - Diouf, 2000s forward (2, 5)
22 Reds are proud to wear it (5)
23 Billy Liddell's book was titled - - Soccer - - - - - (2, 5)

Down

2 Reds defender played Cup Final with this fractured (10)
3 Samuel - - - - - - - -, first Reds striker to score hat-trick against Manchester United (8)
4 Call a fellow Liverpool player, perhaps! (4)
5 Football governing body, based on Hitzigweg, Zurich (4)
6 Tidy play seen by one at Anfield, apparently (4)
9 Injuries may cause managers to fret (5)
10 1999/2000s, Reds striker from Holland (4, 6)
12 Albert Stubbins was the Reds talent spotter (5)
13 Player making his first appearance for a club (8)
18 London Square home of the Football Association (4)
19 Currency needed to buy tickets for 1977 and 1984 European Cup finals (4)
20 Drawn cup tie may go to re - - - - (4)

Crossword No. 34

Across

1 Not the right decision at Anfield (5)
7 1970–80s, midfielder Sammy Lee scored this amount of goals whilst at Anfield (8)
8 ----- Diao, Reds midfielder (5)
10 Train station for Liverpool (4, 6)
12 Sharp goalscorers (8)
14 San ----, famous Italian stadium, scene of infamous Liverpool night in 1965 European Cup (4)
16 Player income (4)
17 Ex-Reds Nigel Clough had this amount of England caps (8)
20 Gary ----------, 2000s midfielder signed from Coventry (10)
23 Jimmy Greaves's endearing name for Ian St John (5)
24 Nottingham Forest and England midfielder, just like Nigel Clough, but he moved to Old Trafford (4, 4)
25 Has Tony Hateley also played for this Villa side, apparently (5)

Down

1 Sweats and squanders a good chance (anag) (6)
2 ---- Ruddock, 1990s defender nicknamed "Razor" (4)
3 2000s, Reds Emile Heskey goes the distance, apparently (4)
4 ----- Burkinshaw, ex-Reds defender and later opposing manager (5)
5 The Reds were the first to be on TV's Match of the Day (9)
6 Fast and tricky footballing move involving numbers (3, 3)
9 Amount of England caps Reds Phil Neal gained (5)
11 Former Scottish-born 1910s Reds forward (3, 6)
13 Brazilian city where a trio of Reds may be found, apparently (3)
15 Star sign of Jerzy Dudek (5)
16 Not Liverpool men's football (6)
18 ------ Heath, former name of team defeated by Liverpool in 2003 Worthington Cup (6)
19 Bruce Grobbelaar's autobiography, *Bring on the* ----- (5)
21 Bench players (4)
22 Nickname of club from which defender Mark Wright joined Reds (4)

1			2		■	3	■	4	■	5	■	6
	■	■		■	7							
8				9	■		■		■		■	
	■	■	10									
	■	11	■		■	■	■		■		■	
12						13		■	14			
■	■		■		■		■	15	■		■	■
16				■	17							18
	■		■	19	■	■	■		■		■	
20						21			22	■	■	
	■		■		■		■	23				
24								■		■	■	
	■		■		■		■	25				

Crossword No. 35

Across

6 2000s Liverpool trainee forward, squad number 34 in 2003–04 season (6, 6)
8 Run with the ball individually (7)
9 ----- Wall, 1960s/70s Reds defender (5)
10 Part of foot used for cheeky pass backwards (4)
12 Loyal players ------ at Anfield, maybe! (6)
14 Ronnie -----, 1950s/60s left sided defender (5)
15 Penalty kicks can be scored, saved or ------ (6)
16 The portents for Liverpool sides on 15 March are not good, apparently (4)
19 Material for football shirts in the 1970s (5)
21 Dynamo ------- ko'd the Reds in European Cup tie 1979–80 (7)
22 1960s, Reds Kevin Lewis played in this position (7, 5)

Down

1 Old-style physios or running shoes (8)
2 Jon -----, 1990s/2000s striker who sounds like a rookie (5)
3 Not the lower terrace (5)
4 ------- Wright, 1990s/2000s Reds defender (7)
5 Ex-Reds Joey Jones played ---- back (4)
6 Germany and Reds midfielder (4, 6)
7 1950s Man City and England keeper against whom Billy Liddell scored hat-trick (5, 5)
11 Could John Toshack land a header here in his sleep? Perhaps (3)
12 --- Kennedy, Double-winner at Highbury, European champion at Anfield (3)
13 John --------, 1980s/90s striker who went on to manage another Merseyside club (8)
14 Liverpool had the tightest defence, even if it is the unkindest observation (7)
17 Room for football managers to work out tactics (5)
18 It sounds like the rows in the stands at Anfield made the eyes water (5)
20 In atmospheric game the crowd at Anfield are not quiet (4)

Crossword No. 35

Crossword No. 36

Across

3 --------- Graziani of AS Roma missed penalty in shoot-out 1984 European Cup final (9)

8 The 1984 European Cup and 1991 Worthington Cup finals were decided on penalty shoot- ---- (4)

9 Assistant referees (8)

10 Bronze figure at Anfield of legendary Reds boss, Bill Shankly (6)

13 Joint can be sprained during match (5)

14 Bernard -------, 2000s Reds midfielder signed from Auxerre (7)

15 How 2000s Reds manager Rafael Benitez would describe the sun to his family (3)

16 Jimmy Case and Tommy Smith were these in the 1960s/70s Liverpool midfield (4, 3)

17 Group of players in Liverpool team (5)

21 Florent ------ Pongolle, 2000s Reds forward (6)

22 Items worn by Reds fans of yesteryear (8)

23 One of many on sole of boot (4)

24 Toffees boss, unrelated to Sammy, when the Reds won their first European Cup (6, 3)

Down

1 Facial feature of ex-Reds Ian Rush (9)

2 Not defenders (9)

4 Laws of the game (5)

5 High score against Crystal Palace 1989 season (4, 3)

6 Comfortable Reds victory (4)

7 Nervous managers ---- gum (4)

11 Players making their first appearances (9)

12 Worn by hirsute players such as ex-Reds Patrik Berger (9)

14 --- Welsh, Liverpool manager 1951–56 (3)

15 George -------, famous public announcer at Anfield! (7)

18 ----- Ardiles was Spurs boss when Reds boss was Graeme Souness (5)

19 Michael Owen scoring without an assist might be a ---- effort (4)

20 Alter ride to find 1920s Reds forward, Thomas ---- (4)

1	■	2	■	3	4		5		6		7	
8				■		■		■		■		■
	■		■	■	9							
10						■		■		■		■
	■		■	■		■		■	■	11	■	12
13					■	14						
	■		■	■	15			■	■		■	
16							■	17				
	■		■	■		■	18	■	■		■	
■	19	■	20	■		■	21					
22								■	■		■	
■		■		■		■		■	23			
24									■		■	

Crossword No. 37

Across

1 Showing red card means this has happened (7, 3)
8 Point -- -----, raising an issue at the Reds' AGM (2, 5)
9 The scorer of a hat-trick becomes ---- - of the match ball (5)
10 It's used to keep football socks up! (4)
11 Half a final, maybe! (4)
12 Jerzy ---ek, 2000s Reds goalkeeper (3)
14 Alan -'-----, 1950s/60s Liverpool and England winger (1'5)
15 ------ Fun, legendary Kopite! (6)
18 Local next to the ground, perhaps! (3)
20 ---- Kennedy, ex-Reds defender nicknamed "Barney Rubble" (4)
21 ---- Henderson, former Reds centre-forward (short) (4)
23 Golden Reds player of yesteryear (5)
24 Liverpool players must not lose their footing, perhaps (7)
25 1950s/60s, Reds goalkeeper (4, 6)

Down

1 Star sign of 1990s/2000s Reds striker Patrik Berger (7)
2 If an opposing defender ---- off, will his nightmares involve Michael Owen (4)
3 Ex-Reds striker Ronny Rosenthal's national team (6)
4 Park here for Merseyside derby match (8)
5 Financially punished by the club (5)
6 English club Graeme Souness managed 1996–97 (11)
7 Ohio born ex-Reds goalkeeper (4, 7)
13 Reds supporters will argue who was the -------- player of all time! (8)
16 In the 1960s and 1970s this person treated injured playes with a magic sponge (7)
17 Markus ------, 2000s Reds defender (6)
19 Show your support of the Reds by wearing emblem (5)
22 Level pitch (4)

Crossword No. 38

Across

1 First, Reserve, Youth and Women's, all are part of Liverpool Football Club (5)
4 -----, Thompson, Cormack and Beardsley, Liverpool stars one and all (5)
10 PFA for instance (5)
11 Eric Anderson was a non-professional player when signing for the Reds (7)
12 Even Michael Owen has nightmare misses at this target (4, 4)
13 You won't stop this hunk for dust, to boot (anag) (4)
15 Football pundit like Mark Lawrenson (6)
17 First goal of a match (6)
19 Tone down a referee's pad (anag) (4)
20 Discover age when showing match on TV, apparently (8)
23 Old-fashioned roofless places where men stood at half-time (7)
24 Not a tight back four (5)
25 Ability like good Liverpool players possess (5)
26 Dick -----, 1920s/30s Reds winger, who played 170 games in six seasons (5)

Down

2 How a banished player might consider his time spent in Liverpool's reserves (5)
3 Fagan and Shankly for instance (8)
5 Michael Owen never asked for transfer in ages, apparently (4)
6 Ex-Reds Nick Barmby was signed from this club (7)
7 The Reds first won this trophy in 1977 (8, 3)
8 Where Liverpool played Flamengo in 1981 and Independiente in 1984 (5)
9 Graeme Souness signed this 'keeper from the Reds in 2000 (4, 7)
14 Pleaded for penalty (8)
16 ------- Gordon, first player to move from Everton to Liverpool (7)
18 *Crazy* -----, title of Emlyn Hughes's book (5)
21 "You'll never walk -----" as it is sung at Anfield (5)
22 Ex-Reds defender or a free-kick defence! (4)

■	1	2		3		■	4	5		6		■
7	■		■		■	8	■		■		■	9
10					■	11						
	■		■		■		■		■		■	
12								■	13			
	■	■	■		■		■	14	■		■	
15		16				■	17					
	■		■		■	18	■		■	■	■	
19				■	20					21		
	■		■	22	■		■		■		■	
23							■	24				
	■		■		■		■		■		■	
■	25					■	26					■

Crossword No. 39

Across

1 Reason for disallowed goal, perhaps (7)
7 On a big match day, all - - - - - lead to Anfield (5)
8 Gathered up in FA Cup tie (7)
9 Jack - - - - - -, 1930s/40s/50s Reds forward (6)
11 Italian side who beat the Reds 1991–92 UEFA cup tie (5)
13 Chops football manager (4)
14 Jim - - - - - - -, 1960s Reds goalkeeper (7)
15 Chooses a post when selection between two players (anag) (4)
16 Tannoy system at Anfield upsets fans, apparently (5)
17 Peter Beardsley had hairy facial features, apparently (6)
21 2000s, Reds Igor Biscan's national team (7)
22 Nickname of ex-Reds defender, Neil Ruddock (5)
23 The first country Liverpool ever visited in a European Cup tie (7)

Down

2 Oslo born 1990s/2000s Reds defender (5, 5)
3 Good farewells when the Reds are leaving (4, 4)
4 Birmingham City and Liverpool - - - - the Worthington Cup final before the Reds won on penalties (4)
5 Liverpool won the Coca-- - - - Cup 1995 (4)
6 Big cheese from near Amsterdam made a comeback! (anag) (4)
9 Players break them (5)
10 Not a Liverpool fan but from Liverpool though! (10)
12 Turf at Anfield (5)
13 England World Cup-winner and clubmate of Emlyn Hughes before they became cross-Stanley Park rivals at club level and international teammates (4, 4)
18 Jan Molby arrived from this Dutch side (4)
19 Face the fall (4)
20 First name of Frenchman who scored winning goal against Liverpool in 1996 FA Cup final (4)

Crossword No. 40

Across

1 Aim for goal (5)
7 Club from which Liverpool signed winger Jimmy Carter (8)
8 - - - - - Clough, 1990s ex-Reds forward (5)
10 1930s, long serving Wales and Liverpool full-back (3, 7)
12 Pegguy - - - - - - - -, Reds keeper released 2003 (8)
14 - - - - play award for well behaved teams (4)
16 Soil at Anfield not Burnley's - - - - Moor though! (4)
17 Road where giant killing exit for Reds took place 1970 FA Cup tie (8)
20 Anfield pitch test (10)
23 Ronnie Whelan managed - - - - -end United 1995–97 (5)
24 Manager's choice voting for new vice-captain (8)
25 National cup won by striker John Toshack before joining Reds (5)

Down

1 Second name of teenage signing M. Pongolle, from Le Havre (6)
2 It is considered bad business to - - - -pay for a player (4)
3 Bring a ball under instant control, lethally once could say (4)
4 Lumps reveal down turn in form (anag) (5)
5 He brings us football pictures (9)
6 The result of Elisha Scott being born in Belfast is he was a - - - - - -man (anag) (6)
9 Billy - - - - -, 1910s/20s Reds half-back (5)
11 Male football athletes (9)
13 - - - Cohen, ex-Reds defender born in Cairo (3)
15 Milan - - - - -, 2000s forward, signed from Banik Ostrava (5)
16 Boot oiled for hard work at the training ground, apparently (6)
18 Liverpool won 1st division title for - - - - - - time, 1972–73 (6)
19 Confusingly these have always been in some stands (5)
21 Ex-Reds forward - - - - Hateley signed from Chelsea 1967 (4)
22 No Newcastle United game involve any goals, apparently (4)

Crossword No. 41

Across

6 Moenchengladbach midfielder who lost to Liverpool in both the 1973 UEFA Cup and 1977 European Cup finals (6, 6)
8 How championships were decided until the 1970s: goal - - - - - - - (7)
9 1989–90, the Reds won the Division One - - - - - (5)
10 Direction found when the Reds arrive at Upton Park (4)
12 Tom - - - - - -, 1930s/40s Reds defender not comedian Tommy though! (6)
14 2000s Liverpool born English Premiership player, Kevin - - - - - (5)
15 When ex-Red Ray Kennedy played for Arsenal he was one (nick) (6)
16 Employs the ball (4)
19 A warden may give Liverpool player a medal, apparently (5)
21 City-centre hotel which has staged many Liverpool FC functions (7)
22 1990s/2000s, Liverpool and Finland international (4, 8)

Down

1 Title of Michael Owen's first autobiography (2, 6)
2 Received in cup final (5)
3 Ex-Reds midfielder Paul Ince signed from - - - - - Milan (5)
4 Lime Street is Liverpool's main one (7)
5 Back or wing not right though! (4)
6 Ex-Reds Ray Houghton was not a scouser (10)
7 Great dark days of 1920s/30s bad Liverpool sides (10)
11 They are not goals against when Liverpool score (3)
12 International headwear (3)
13 Call off Liverpool match! (8)
14 1904–08 Liverpool and Scotland goalkeeper (3, 4)
17 - - - - - Burrows, former Liverpool defender (5)
18 Mates in Liverpool sides (anag) (5)
20 - - - - Kennedy, Sunderland born ex-Reds defender (4)

Crossword No. 42

Across

3 1960s/70s, Reds midfielder (5, 4)
8 Nickname of the club which sold Kevin Keegan to Liverpool (4)
9 Star sign of Jamie Carragher (8)
10 Anthony Le – – – – – –, teenage signing from Le Havre, 2003 (6)
13 Under-– – – – –, rolled the ball to a teammate, or short of fire-power maybe (5)
14 Ex-Reds Peter Beardsley joined this club 1991 (7)
15 – – – Fagan, Reds boss 1983–85 (3)
16 Tough guy Graeme Souness was not soft (4, 3)
17 Christian – – – – –, 2000s defender and German international (5)
21 Is this where Dean Saunders and Mark Wright got their football degrees? (6)
22 Decade in which Graeme Souness was Liverpool manager (8)
23 – – – – Livermore, 1960s/70s Reds midfielder (4)
24 Became chief executive of Liverpool 1998 (4, 5)

Down

1 – – – – – – – – – Frankfurt, played the Reds in 1973 UEFA Cup (9)
2 Stan – – – – – – – – –, ex-Reds striker (9)
4 Slow or quick to, perhaps! (5)
5 Language resulting in sending-off (7)
6 Kopite's favourite player, maybe (4)
7 Football hooligan (4)
11 Jon – – – – – – – – –, 2000s squad player, wore the No. 36 shirt in 2003–04 season (9)
12 Not the favourites (9)
14 Ray Clemence once saved penalty in this age, apparently (3)
15 Ex-Reds John Barnes was born in this country (7)
18 Not the winner (5)
19 – – – – Hamann, 1990s/2000s Liverpool midfielder (short) (4)
20 Unlike ex-Reds Geoff Strong (4)

1	■	2	■	3	4		5		6		7	
8				■		■		■		■		■
	■		■	■	9							
10						■		■		■		■
	■		■	■		■		■	■	11	■	12
13					■	14						
	■		■	■	15			■	■		■	
16							■	17				
	■		■	■		■	18	■	■		■	
■	19	■	20	■		■	21					
22								■	■		■	
■		■		■		■		■	23			
24									■		■	

Crossword No. 43

Across

1 Knocked out Liverpool from the 2003–04 FA Cup (10)
8 Nationality of Paul Ince's team mates at Inter Milan, maybe (7)
9 Only one for a draw (5)
10 Phil Thompson's first game as temporary manager was against Dynamo - - - - (4)
11 Dixie - - - -, presented Kevin Keegan with PFA award (4)
12 Relationship of 1990s Reds striker Dean Saunders to 1940s/50s Reds striker Roy Saunders (3)
14 - - - - - - Wenger was the losing manager in the 2001 FA Cup Final (6)
15 Not an outside position for Roger Hunt (6)
18 Football outcome (short) (3)
20 Harry - - - -ham, 1930s/40s Reds forward (4)
21 Pest the keeper about taking one! (anag) (4)
23 Dean - - - - -, where Jamie Redknapp played before joining the Reds in 1991 (5)
24 Tom -'- - - - - -, scouse comedian (1'6)
25 1970s, Geordie and ex-Liverpool striker (4, 6)

Down

1 Squad members (7)
2 Reasons for umbrella at Anfield (4)
3 - - - - - - Westerveld, ex-Reds Dutch goalkeeper (6)
4 Rival on the pitch (8)
5 Away journeys for Reds fans (5)
6 Roger - - - - - - - - - - -, referee involved in controversial 1970s Liverpool game (11)
7 Separates Anfield from Goodison (7, 4)
13 Go on a run without losing (8)
16 Pressure can be - - - - - - - for football managers (7)
17 Italian Serie A side Liverpool have beaten in the past (1,1, 4)
19 Anatomically the part of the body used for headers! (5)
22 - - - -work, the goal frame although not that substance now! (4)

Crossword No. 44

Across

1 ----- Kippe, 1990s/2000s Reds defender (5)
4 Sandy -----, once scored own goal in derby match in Reds favour (5)
10 Chris Lawler played at ------back for Liverpool (5)
11 ------- Wilson, former Reds player not Mr Chaplin though! (7)
12 Liverpool is not a Southern team (8)
13 ---- Litmanen, ex-Reds forward (4)
15 Bruce Grobbelaar also played for this Athletic club (6)
17 Fans on the Kop noisily raise a glass to toast another Liverpool goal! (6)
19 Magpies and other fans enjoy a half-time snack apparently (4)
20 Tommy --------, ex-Liverpool goalkeeper (8)
23 Bernard ------- , 1930s/40s Liverpool defender (7)
24 Brought ire down on exhausted players apparently (5)
25 Routine in training for the red army (5)
26 Leg joints often injured (5)

Down

2 ----- Hunt, legend at Anfield (5)
3 Englishman for Ray Clemence, -------- for Sander Westerveld (8)
5 Steve McManaman joined ---- Madrid from Liverpool (4)
6 Gordon ------- , 1960s Scottish Reds forward (7)
7 Third Merseyside team play here (7, 4)
8 One type of draw (5)
9 Ex-Reds and Toffees midfielder (5, 6)
14 Athletic team who won at Anfield for the first time in 50 years in 2004 (8)
16 Forename of 1990s/2000s Reds and Germany midfielder, Mr Hamann (7)
18 Jimmy -----, 1940s/50s Liverpool winger (5)
21 Phil Neal kept his when taking penalties (5)
22 Football icon like Kevin Keegan! (4)

■	1	2		3		■	4	5		6		■
7	■		■		■	8	■		■		■	9
10					■	11						
	■		■		■		■		■		■	
12								■	13			
	■	■	■		■		■	14	■		■	
15		16				■	17					
	■		■		■	18	■		■	■	■	
19				■	20					21		
	■		■	22	■		■		■		■	
23							■	24				
	■		■		■		■		■		■	
■	25					■	26					■

Crossword No. 45

Across

1 Tremendous ex-Reds goalscorer (3, 4)
7 Colour of Liverpool shirts when they played at Nottingham Forest in first ever Sky Sports live match (5)
8 Red swan strolls from Bolton or Wolverhampton (anag) (7)
9 Attacking set-piece from a quadrant (6)
11 Anfield season ticket holder is the ----- of his! (5)
13 Sponsor's emblem on a shirt! (4)
14 Nationality of ex-Reds striker, Ronnie Rosenthal (7)
15 Football hero for adoring fan (4)
16 Forename of first Liverpool captain to lift the European Cup (5)
17 Woman invited to unveil Shankly Gates at 1982 ceremony (6)
21 David -------, 1970s/80s Reds forward (7)
22 Jimmy -----, ex-Reds forward (5)
23 Forename of Liverpool midfielder, Mr Diomede (7)

Down

2 1970s, ex-Reds striker (4, 6)
3 Matt Busby was a Red as a player, but a --- ----- as a manager (3, 5)
4 San ----, 1990s/2000s midfielder Paul Ince's home ground immediately before Anfield (4)
5 Three goals creates a riot (anag) (4)
6 ---- Saunders, ex-Reds striker (4)
9 What a Liverpool goal at Anfield brings from the Kop (5)
10 Year of Liverpool's fourth European Cup win ------ ---- (6, 4)
12 Club from which Rob Jones and Danny Murphy were bought (5)
13 Jari --------, ex-Reds and Finland striker (8)
18 Four---- rule, something Ray Clemence had to be aware of! (4)
19 "They think it's all over; -- -- now" (2, 2)
20 "Walk on with ---- in your heart" (4)

LIVERPOOL
FOOTBALL CLUB
EST 1892

WALK ALONE

Crossword No. 46

Across

1 FC Swarovski - - - - -, Austrian opponents of Liverpool (5)
7 Result of the 1986 FA Cup Final, Liverpool v. Everton (5, 3)
8 - - - - - Spackman, 1980s Reds midfielder (5)
10 Welsh international, played over 300 games for Liverpool (3, 7)
12 Unfastened the boot laces (8)
14 - - - - Hickson, forward signed from Everton in November 1959 for £40,500 (4)
16 A leaf out of Kevin Keegan's book (4)
17 Number of players per team who can play in a competitive game, including subs (8)
20 - - - - - - - - - - Scored against Liverpool in the 2001 UEFA Cup Final (4, 6)
23 In 1996 newspapers nicknamed Liverpool the " - - - - - Boys" (5)
24 Ex-Reds and Israeli international (3, 5)
25 Way in at Anfield (5)

Down

1 Where the "This is Anfield" sign is touched by players (6)
2 The game is finished when Liverpool play Blackburn Rovers, apparently (4)
3 - - - - Thompson, 1970s/80s Liverpool captain (4)
4 Football sides (5)
5 Not away matches for Liverpool (4, 5)
6 Ron Yeats' position was - - - - - - -half (6)
9 What used to hold the bladder in a leather football (5)
11 1910s forward signed from Everton, but who died in Glasgow in 1915 aged 26 (3, 6)
13 Pride goes before a fall, apparently (3)
15 Liverpool Box where journalists report on Anfield matches (5)
16 Robert - - - - - -, 1940s S. African winger, kept out of the Liverpool side by Billy Liddell (6)
18 Amount of minutes in football match (6)
19 Ground where 1980s defender Mark Lawrenson was manager (5)
21 Michael - - - -, 1990s Liverpool revelation (4)
22 The Anfield ground is on match days (4)

WALK ALONE

Crossword No. 47

Across

6 Nickname of ex-Reds defender Alan Kennedy (6, 6)
8 Flags for the Kop (7)
9 Star sign of ex-Reds striker, David Johnson (5)
10 – – – – Xavier, 2000s Reds and Portugal defender (4)
12 Assault the Liverpool forward line (6)
14 Not a late kick-off at Anfield (5)
15 Rapid raider who sounds like striker David, who was a Red for eight months in 1991 (6)
16 Cup won three times by Liverpool, first in 1973 (4)
19 Vote for team selection like they did in old days, apparently (5)
21 – – – – – – – Longworth, 1910s/20s Reds and England captain (7)
22 1990s, Birkenhead born midfielder (5, 7)

Down

1 Merseyside club which Tommy Lawrence joined in 1970 (8)
2 Shirt number of Keegan or Dalglish (5)
3 Football nationality of Preston-born Mark Lawrenson (5)
4 Football skill (7)
5 In terms of League titles, Liverpool are the most successful – – – – in England (4)
6 Former Liverpool manager (3, 7)
7 1930s/40s/50s, Liverpool striker (4, 6)
11 George – – –, Liverpool boss 1936–50 (3)
12 – – – Arrowsmith, ex-Reds striker 1961–69 (3)
13 Save rage for median statistics (anag) (8)
14 Match programme issue, maybe! (7)
17 Liverpool hairstyles of the 1970s (5)
18 Liverpool went in front with a header, apparently (5)
20 Steven Gerrard sets an example for this test, apparently (4)

Crossword No. 48

Across

3 Steve ---------, teammate of Robbie Fowler at Anfield and City of Manchester Stadium (9)
8 Chase for the title (4)
9 Goalkeeper joined Liverpool from Chesterfield 1905 (3, 5)
10 Goalkeepers wear these for grip, but outfield players now do so for warmth (6)
13 Notice the rage in Rangers side, apparently (5)
14 John Toshack was signed from this Welsh club (7)
15 Match suspension (3)
16 Liverpool won the ---- --- in 1984 (4, 3)
17 Nationality of ex-Reds forward, Patrik Berger (short) (5)
21 Surname of cross-city striking partner for Michael Owen on England duty (6)
22 Call match off at Anfield (8)
23 A Reds win wouldn't lead to a celebration at Galatasaray apparently (4)
24 Ex-Reds forward Jack Whitham signed from this day club (9)

Down

1 Matchday publication (9)
2 Jimmy ---------, 1920s/30s Liverpool utility player (9)
4 Sec is a French international forward, Djibril, linked with the Reds in 2004 (anag) (5)
5 Italian side who were at home in the 1984 European Cup final, but still lost! (1, 1, 5)
6 ---- Hansen, ex-Reds captain (4)
7 John Aldridge's nickname (4)
11 Ex-Reds Peter Cormack had two stints with this Scottish side (9)
12 Young Player -- --- ---- 2001, award won by Steven Gerrard (2, 3, 4)
14 Tommy Smith only gained one for England (3)
15 David -------, signed from WBA 1988 (7)
18 A near venue for Anfield (anag) (5)
19 When you never walk alone, have this in your heart (4)
20 Nuts the ball and shock Liverpool (anag) (4)

1	■	2	■	3	4		5		6		7	
8				■		■		■		■		■
	■		■	■	9							
10						■		■		■		■
	■		■	■		■		■	■	11	■	12
13					■	14						
	■		■	■	15			■	■		■	
16							■	17				
	■		■	■		■	18	■	■		■	
■	19	■	20	■		■	21					
22								■	■		■	
■		■		■		■		■	23			
24									■		■	

Crossword No. 49

Across

1 1970s/80s, Liverpool defender (5, 5)
8 1950s Reds Alan A'Court was signed from ------- Cables (7)
9 Bruno -----, missed penalty 1984 European Cup final (5)
10 The sort of weather clubs look for when going abroad for winter training breaks (4)
11 Part of the body to score goals, perhaps! (4)
12 Cup fixture (3)
14 Type of league such as the Lancashire League Liverpool won in 1892–93 (6)
15 Slack defending pundit Alan Hansen would say! (6)
18 Reverse pot for League position Liverpool like to be! (3)
20 ---- Alonso, scored against Reds UEFA 2001 final (4)
21 Nickname shared by 1930s forward Thomas Johnson and 1960s/70s forward John Toshack (4)
23 Dick -----, lost his Liverpool place to Ron Yeats (5)
24 Americans would say Jimmy Case struck ball with ------- power (7)
25 Area including and around Liverpool (10)

Down

1 Bruno -------, 2000s Reds French midfielder (7)
2 ---- Poznan were beat by Reds 1985 in European Cup tie (4)
3 Caught fish after you've scored (6)
4 Spotland club where 1930s Reds outside-left Adolf Hanson was a wartime guest (8)
5 ----- John, ex-Reds and Scotland international (3, 2)
6 John Wark arrived at Liverpool from this club (7, 4)
7 Year the first FA Premier League season ended (6, 5)
13 Dashing looking forwards (8)
16 Rise a division, maybe! (7)
17 Birds on club badges: Liver for Liverpool, Seagull for Brighton & Hove Albion and ------ for Norwich City (6)
19 Does every player have his! (5)
22 Not quite the final (4)

Crossword No. 50

Across

1 - - - - - Strong was the first ever Liverpool substitute to play in a League match (5)
4 Paul - - - - -, 1980s Liverpool striker signed from Luton Town (5)
10 Portuguese side who Liverpool beat in the 2001 UEFA Cup (5)
11 Liverpool goalscoring legend (3, 4)
12 Roger Hunt was in 1966 a member of the - - - - - - - - - winning team (5, 3)
13 When Liverpool played away to Galatasary, banners at the stadium said, "Welcome to - - - -" (4)
15 Reds Kenny Dalglish signed from this Scottish club (6)
17 Mrs Paisley, represented her late husband Bob as a guest of honour when the standing Kop closed in 1994 (6)
19 Nickname of Thomas Bradshaw, 6ft 2in Reds 1930s centre-half (4)
20 Vocally supporting from the Kop (8)
23 Team Don Hutchison left Liverpool for (4, 3)
24 Alter wader for whisky-sponsored Shield Liverpool won 1906 (anag) (5)
25 Gerry - - - - -, 1950s/60s Liverpool left-back (5)
26 2000s French midfielder, - - - - - Cheyrou (5)

Down

2 An own goal is a footballing mistake (5)
3 Night game is visible at Anfield (8)
5 John - - - - Riise, 2000s Liverpool defender (4)
6 Graeme - - - - - - -, former Liverpool captain (7)
7 Liverpool signed ex-striker David Johnston from this side (7, 4)
8 El Hadji - - - - -, 2000s Liverpool forward (5)
9 Contenders for the title! (11)
14 Position associated with ex-Reds player, Alan Hansen (8)
16 Alec - - - - - - -, left-back in the 1974 FA Cup final (7)
18 Victorious Liverpool player (short) (5)
21 Colin - - - - -, former Liverpool defender (5)
22 Pad protects this part of the leg (4)

The Solutions

No. 1

		B	O	B	P	A	I	S	L	E	Y	
E		L		A		B		O		M		E
M	C	I	N	N	E	S		C	O	L	I	N
I		N		S		E		I		Y		G
L	O	D	Z		I	N	G	E		N	I	L
E		E		T		T		D				A
H	A	R	V	E	Y		H	A	M	A	N	N
E				R		O		D		B		D
S	I	R		R	U	L	E		H	U	N	T
K		A		I		E		S		S		E
E	R	N	I	E		A	M	E	R	I	C	A
Y		G		R		R		M		V		M
	M	E	R	S	E	Y	S	I	D	E		

No. 2

	I	A	N	S	T		R	E	A	C	H	
M		C		T		M		V		A		B
I	N	T	E	R		A	D	E	L	P	H	I
C		O		E		R		N		T		L
H	A	R	K	N	E	S	S		K	A	R	L
A				G		H		A		I		S
E	I	G	H	T	H		C	L	I	N	C	H
L		L		H		R		A				A
O	M	A	R		J	O	H	N	S	T	O	N
W		S		W		W		B		H		K
E	N	G	L	A	N	D		A	P	R	I	L
N		O		V		Y		L		E		Y
	O	W	N	E	R		B	L	U	E	S	

No. 3

I	A	N	R	U	S	H		B		F		
	P		O		O		D	A	K	A	R	
O	P	E	N	I	N	G		R		I		
	E		Y		G		A	N	D	R	E	W
T	A	K	E	R			H				L	
	R		A		B		E		G	A	I	N
	A		T	E	R	R	A	C	E		M	
E	N	D	S		I		D		N		I	
	C				A			M	I	L	N	E
L	E	S	S	O	N		M		U		A	
		A		W		W	E	B	S	I	T	E
	D	U	D	E	K		N		E		E	
		L		N		O	U	T	S	I	D	E

No. 4

R	O	O	M	S		F		C		O		I
O			A		H	O	O	L	I	G	A	N
N	I	N	T	H		R		A		R		C
N			T	O	M	M	Y	S	M	I	T	H
I		P		O				S		Z		E
E	U	R	O	P	E	A	N		B	O	Y	S
		O		S		V		P		V		
H	I	G	H		F	I	N	A	L	I	S	T
A		R		A				P		C		A
M	C	A	L	L	I	S	T	E	R			U
A		M		T		T		R	O	G	E	R
N	U	M	B	E	R	E	D		M			U
N		E		R		W		J	A	M	E	S

No. 5

		A		D		C		O		S		
P	E	T	E	R	C	O	R	M	A	C	K	
A		H		U		H		I		O		S
C	O	L	O	G	N	E		T	I	T	L	E
E		E		S		N		T				A
M	A	T	E		B		R	E	U	B	E	N
A		I		S	A	V	E	D		E		D
K	I	C	K	E	D		D		A	L	O	U
E				A		V		B		G		N
R	E	S	T	S		I	N	J	U	R	E	D
S		N		O		L		O		A		E
	J	O	H	N	A	L	D	R	I	D	G	E
		W		S		A		N		E		

No. 6

M		A		L	A	W	R	E	N	S	O	N
O	U	T	S		L		E		O		G	
U		T			A	M	A	T	E	U	R	S
S	L	A	T	E	R		C		L		E	
T		C			M		H			P		C
A	S	K	E	D		R	E	S	E	R	V	E
C		E			D	U	D			E		N
H	A	R	D	M	E	N		U	P	S	E	T
E		S			F		T			E		E
	Z		F		E		H	A	M	A	N	N
V	I	C	A	R	A	G	E			S		A
	C		I		T		M		F	O	U	R
M	O	R	R	I	S	S	E	Y		N		Y

No. 7

		M	I	L	A	N	B	A	R	O	S	
J		A		U		E		S		L		F
A	T	T	A	C	K	S		H	A	D	J	I
C		U		K		S		W		E		T
K	I	R	K		Z	I	C	O		R	O	N
I		I		H		E		R				E
H	E	S	K	E	Y		S	T	U	F	F	S
I				I		D		H		A		S
T	O	P		G	O	A	L		O	M	I	T
H		O		H		N		A		I		E
A	R	R	O	W		I	S	L	A	N	D	S
M		T		A		S		E		E		T
	B	O	D	Y	C	H	E	C	K	S		

No. 8

	S	T	U	D	S		R	I	G	H	T	
S		R		I		S		C		O		R
E	V	A	N	S		C	R	O	A	T	I	A
N		I		A		R		N		S		Y
D	E	N	I	S	L	A	W		E	P	I	C
I				T		P		R		U		L
N	E	R	V	E	S		G	E	O	R	G	E
G		E		R		F		D				M
S	I	T	S		N	I	C	K	N	A	M	E
O		I		H		E		N		S		N
F	U	R	N	E	L	L		A	N	T	I	C
F		E		E		D		P		O		E
	A	D	O	L	F		O	P	E	N	S	

No. 9

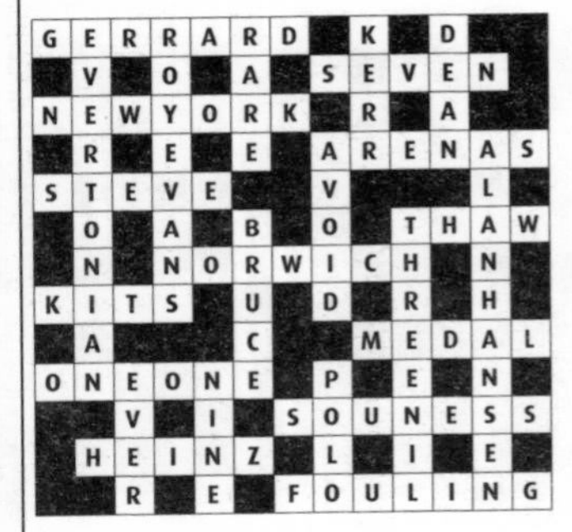

G	E	R	R	A	R	D		K		D		
	V		O		A		S	E	V	E	N	
N	E	W	Y	O	R	K		R		A		
	R		E		E		A	R	E	N	A	S
S	T	E	V	E			V				L	
	O		A		B		O		T	H	A	W
	N		N	O	R	W	I	C	H		N	
K	I	T	S		U		D		R		H	
	A				C			M	E	D	A	L
O	N	E	O	N	E		P		E		N	
		V		I		S	O	U	N	E	S	S
	H	E	I	N	Z		L		I		E	
		R		E		F	O	U	L	I	N	G

No. 10

D	E	B	U	T		J		S		R		C
I			E		C	A	M	P	B	E	L	L
D	E	L	F	I		R		E		L		O
I			A	N	F	I	E	L	D	E	R	S
E		A		T				L		G		E
R	O	Y	K	E	A	N	E		C	A	R	D
		R		R		E		M		T		
S	P	U	R		S	T	R	I	K	E	R	S
A		N		S				N		D		E
N	E	I	L	M	E	L	L	O	R			A
D		T		I		E		R	E	S	T	S
E	J	E	C	T	I	N	G		D			O
R		D		H		S		A	S	T	O	N

No. 11

		A		L		W		P		J		
N	U	M	B	E	R	E	L	E	V	E	N	
I		E		V		L		A		A		F
C	O	R	N	E	R	S		R	I	N	G	O
K		I		L		H		S				R
B	A	C	K		T		R	O	B	B	I	E
A		A		N	O	L	A	N		O		I
R	O	N	N	I	E		Y		L	O	N	G
M				N		C		S		T		N
B	Y	R	N	E		L	U	C	E	R	N	E
Y		O		N		U		A		O		R
	D	A	V	I	D	B	U	R	R	O	W	S
		D		L		S		F		M		

No. 12

E		K		C	A	P	R	I	C	O	R	N
D	O	N	S		L		E		O		O	
D		O			O	F	F	I	C	I	A	L
I	S	T	V	A	N		E		A		D	
E		T			E		R			R		C
G	A	Y	L	E		C	E	N	T	U	R	Y
R		A			O	B	E			N		R
A	B	S	E	N	C	E		C	O	N	T	I
Y		H			O		O			E		L
	H		C		N		M	A	D	R	I	D
P	A	U	L	I	N	C	E			S		O
	L		U		O		N		T	U	R	N
C	L	U	B	C	R	E	S	T		P		E

No. 13

		D	U	B	L	I	N	C	I	T	Y	
I		E		O		N		O		A		G
N	E	R	V	O	U	S		L	I	B	R	A
T		B		S		I		O		L		L
E	X	I	T		O	D	D	S		E	R	A
R		E		C		E		S				T
C	O	S	T	L	Y		R	U	S	S	I	A
I				E		A		S		T		S
T	O	M		M	A	T	T		H	A	K	A
I		I		E		T		N		T		R
E	M	L	Y	N		A	M	E	R	I	C	A
S		N		C		C		S		O		Y
	L	E	V	E	R	K	U	S	E	N		

No. 14

	M	O	L	B	Y		W	E	L	S	H	
P		R		A		C		I		T		J
R	O	G	E	R		I	S	R	A	E	L	I
E		A		R		V		E		W		M
M	E	N	D	I	B	I	L		W	A	R	M
I				E		C		S		R		Y
E	R	R	O	R	S		C	E	L	T	I	C
R		I		S		K		V				A
S	O	C	K		D	E	F	E	N	D	E	R
M		H		D		N		N		E		T
I	T	A	L	I	A	N		N	E	R	V	E
P		R		D		Y		I		B		R
	E	D	D	I	E		L	L	O	Y	D	

No. 15

M	C	M	A	H	O	N		L		K		
	O		R		W		J	A	M	I	E	
F	L	O	P	P	E	D		T		N		
	L		H		N		K	E	E	G	A	N
G	A	T	E	S			E				C	
	R		X		R		B		D	I	C	K
	B		A	V	E	R	A	G	E		R	
R	O	A	D		V		B		F		I	
	N				I			D	E	A	N	O
G	E	O	R	G	E		H		N		G	
		N		L		P	U	N	D	I	T	S
	D	U	D	E	K		L		E		O	
		S		N		F	L	O	R	E	N	T

No. 16

G	L	E	N	N		Z		N		F		O
R			E		D	E	N	I	S	L	A	W
A	L	L	A	N		R		C		Y		N
E			L	O	C	O	M	O	T	I	V	E
M		M		L				L		N		R
E	X	C	H	A	N	G	E		A	G	E	S
		D		N		O		S		P		
N	O	E	L		C	A	P	T	A	I	N	S
I		R		P				E		G		H
N	U	M	B	E	R	F	I	V	E			E
I		O		R		R		E	R	N	I	E
A	T	T	A	C	K	E	R		O			D
N		T		Y		E		A	S	K	E	Y

No. 17

		I		V		A		R		G		
R	O	N	N	I	E	W	H	E	L	A	N	
A		J		R		A		D		L		A
Y	O	U	N	G	E	R		S	H	A	R	P
L		R		O		D		T				P
A	V	I	V		D		P	A	S	S	E	R
M		E		R	O	V	E	R		T		E
B	I	S	C	A	N		T		B	A	R	N
E				T		K		W		N		T
R	I	G	H	T		E	L	H	A	D	J	I
T		L		L		I		I		A		C
	S	E	V	E	N	T	Y	T	H	R	E	E
		N		S		H		E		D		

No. 18

P		P		M	C	M	A	N	A	M	A	N
A	L	E	C		O		B		C		L	
U		N			H	E	I	G	H	W	A	Y
L	E	A	G	U	E		L		E		N	
W		L			N		I			H		S
A	F	T	E	R		S	T	E	W	A	R	T
L		I			R	O	Y			L		E
S	T	E	P	H	E	N		U	N	F	I	T
H		S			B		L			T		I
	M		B		O		O	N	S	I	D	E
S	E	L	L	O	U	T	S			M		N
	R		U		N		E		S	E	A	N
D	E	F	E	N	D	E	R	S		S		E

No. 19

		M	A	R	K	W	R	I	G	H	T	
D		A		U		I		N		O		S
A	R	S	E	N	A	L		J	A	M	I	E
N		C		S		S		U		E		N
N	O	O	N		F	O	U	R		S	A	D
Y		T		Y		N		I				I
M	O	S	C	O	W		G	E	R	M	A	N
U				U		H		S		A		G
R	O	B		N	E	A	L		A	L	M	S
P		R		G		N		I		C		O
H	O	U	S	E		S	E	N	T	O	F	F
Y		N		S		E		C		L		F
	N	O	T	T	I	N	G	H	A	M		

No. 20

	S	T	O	K	E		O	F	F	E	R	
M		W		E		A		I		N		K
A	L	I	E	N		R	E	F	E	R	E	E
R		C		B		I		A		O		V
T	E	E	N	A	G	E	R		L	U	Z	I
I				T		S		L		T		N
N	U	M	B	E	R		B	I	C	E	P	S
T		C		S		M		M				H
Y	E	A	R		N	E	G	A	T	I	V	E
L		T		S		A		S		T		E
E	V	E	R	T	O	N		S	T	A	N	D
R		E		A		S		O		L		Y
	F	R	A	N	C		P	L	A	Y	S	

No. 21

S	A	N	S	I	R	O		M		P		
	S		E		U		P	O	O	L	S	
S	T	A	N	D	B	Y		O		A		
	O		D		S		A	R	E	N	A	S
E	N	J	O	Y			B				T	
	V		F		R		B		S	A	M	I
	I		F	L	O	R	E	N	T		O	
P	L	U	S		Y		Y		A		S	
	L				L			J	U	M	P	S
W	A	D	D	L	E		H		N		H	
		R		I		B	E	A	T	L	E	S
	W	A	L	S	H		R		O		R	
		W		T		F	O	U	N	D	E	D

No. 22

R	I	G	H	T		S		B		A		L
E			A		A	T	T	I	T	U	D	E
T	A	I	L	S		A		L		T		A
I			L	A	R	R	Y	L	L	O	Y	D
R		T		V				Y		M		E
E	A	S	Y	E	A	S	Y		F	A	I	R
		V		D		I		J		T		
T	I	M	E		F	R	E	E	K	I	C	K
A		U		S				E		C		E
L	A	N	C	A	S	H	I	R	E			T
L		I		L		I		S	A	I	N	T
E	X	C	H	A	N	G	E		S			L
C		H		D		H		S	T	E	V	E

No. 23

		T		H		K		L		C		
B	A	R	R	Y	V	E	N	I	S	O	N	
O		A		S		I		N		L		H
B	E	N	N	E	T	T		D	R	A	M	A
P		M		N		H		S				I
A	B	E	L		C		L	A	W	L	E	R
I		R		B	O	G	E	Y		O		S
S	T	E	A	L	S		G		P	O	S	T
L				A		F		A		S		Y
E	V	A	N	S		L	I	D	D	E	L	L
Y		R		T		O		D		N		E
	I	N	T	E	R	P	R	E	T	E	R	S
		E		D		S		D		D		

No. 24

G		G		M	C	D	E	R	M	O	T	T
I	R	O	N		H		V		A		O	
L		R			E	L	E	C	T	I	N	G
L	A	D	I	E	S		R		E		Y	
E		O			T		T			C		S
S	A	N	D	Y		N	O	U	C	A	M	P
P		L			E	O	N			M		O
I	R	E	L	A	N	D		C	H	E	E	R
E		E			Q		G			R		T
	U		P		U		R	I	V	A	L	S
T	E	L	E	V	I	S	E			M		M
	F		E		R		E		S	A	V	E
K	A	R	L	H	E	I	N	Z		N		N

No. 25

		S	U	P	P	O	R	T	E	R	S	
T		A		O		L		E		E		A
R	E	L	A	T	E	D		R	I	V	E	R
A		V		S		H		R		I		T
B	R	A	D		G	A	L	A		E	P	H
Z		G		C		M		C				U
O	L	E	A	R	Y		M	E	R	C	E	R
N				I		B		D		H		R
S	U	B		M	E	A	L		S	E	M	I
P		A		I		R		E		E		L
O	L	D	E	N		R	E	S	E	R	V	E
R		G		A		E		S		E		Y
	K	E	M	L	Y	N	R	O	A	D		

No. 26

	W	H	I	T	E		M	A	R	S	H	
P		U		H		R		W		W		B
H	O	R	S	E		A	M	A	T	E	U	R
I		S		S		V		Y		D		A
L	I	T	M	A	N	E	N		B	I	R	D
B				I		N		T		S		F
O	Y	V	I	N	D		A	R	T	H	U	R
E		E		T		H		A				I
R	A	N	G		J	O	H	N	A	R	N	E
S		I		B		U		S		O		D
M	U	S	C	L	E	S		F	R	O	D	E
A		O		U		E		E		M		L
	K	N	E	E	S		I	R	I	S	H	

No. 27

R	A	I	N	I	N	G		S		U		
	B		I		E		W	A	L	E	S	
K	E	N	N	E	T	H		M		F		
	L		E		S		S	I	N	A	M	A
E	X	I	T	S			T				A	
	A		E		S		A		R	U	N	S
	V		E	L	H	A	D	J	I		C	
F	I	N	N		A		E		G		H	
	E				R			L	O	W	E	R
T	R	A	O	R	E		S		B		S	
		L		U		S	E	V	E	N	T	Y
	N	E	V	E	R		M		R		E	
		C		D		F	I	X	T	U	R	E

No. 28

A	F	T	E	R		B		C		C		R
C			V		R	O	C	H	D	A	L	E
O	P	T	E	D		Y		E		M		S
U			N	E	W	S	P	A	P	E	R	S
R		F		R				T		R		I
T	H	R	E	E	T	W	O		G	A	M	E
		A		K		I		U		M		
S	O	N	G		S	T	A	N	D	A	R	D
C		C		D				D		N		I
O	N	E	H	U	N	D	R	E	D			A
U		S		D		R		R	A	Z	O	R
S	O	C	I	E	D	A	D		T			R
E		O		K		W		M	E	L	I	A

No. 29

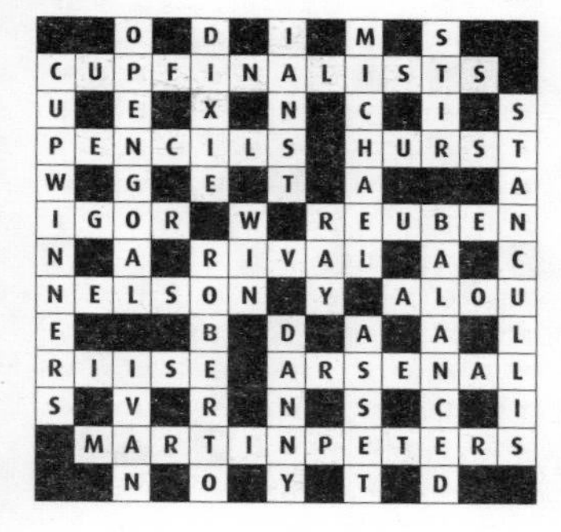

No. 30

No. 31

No. 32

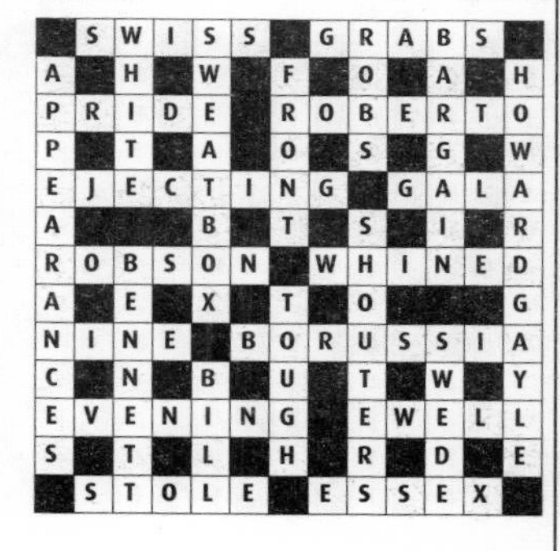

No. 33

S	C	O	R	E	R	S		F		N		
	O		A		I		R	I	V	E	R	
P	L	A	Y	I	N	G		F		A		
	L		B		G		W	A	L	T	E	R
B	A	R	O	N			O				R	
	R		U		S		R		D	O	I	G
	B		L	U	C	E	R	N	E		K	
G	O	L	D		O		Y		B		M	
	N				U			D	U	D	E	K
R	E	S	U	L	T		P		T		I	
		O		I		E	L	H	A	D	J	I
	S	H	I	R	T		A		N		E	
		O		A		M	Y	S	T	O	R	Y

No. 34

W	R	O	N	G		M		K		T		O
A			E		N	I	N	E	T	E	E	N
S	A	L	I	F		L		I		L		E
T			L	I	M	E	S	T	R	E	E	T
E		T		F				H		V		W
S	H	O	O	T	E	R	S		S	I	R	O
		M		Y		I		A		S		
W	A	G	E		F	O	U	R	T	E	E	N
O		R		C				I		D		E
M	C	A	L	L	I	S	T	E	R			W
E		C		O		U		S	A	I	N	T
N	E	I	L	W	E	B	B		M			O
S		E		N		S		A	S	T	O	N

No. 35

		T		N		U		S		L		
D	A	R	R	E	N	P	O	T	T	E	R	
I		A		W		P		E		F		F
D	R	I	B	B	L	E		P	E	T	E	R
I		N		Y		R		H				A
H	E	E	L		N		R	E	M	A	I	N
A		R		M	O	R	A	N		L		K
M	I	S	S	E	D		Y		I	D	E	S
A				A		S		T		R		W
N	Y	L	O	N		T	B	I	L	I	S	I
N		O		E		U		E		D		F
	O	U	T	S	I	D	E	R	I	G	H	T
		D		T		Y		S		E		

No. 36

M		A		F	R	A	N	C	E	S	C	O
O	U	T	S		U		I		A		H	
U		T			L	I	N	E	S	M	E	N
S	T	A	T	U	E		E		Y		W	
T		C			S		N			D		H
A	N	K	L	E		D	I	O	M	E	D	E
C		E			S	O	L			B		A
H	A	R	D	M	E	N		S	Q	U	A	D
E		S			P		O			T		B
	S		R		H		S	I	N	A	M	A
R	O	S	E	T	T	E	S			N		N
	L		I		O		I		S	T	U	D
G	O	R	D	O	N	L	E	E		S		S

No. 37

No. 38

No. 39

No. 40

No. 41

		I		M		I		S		L		
G	U	N	T	E	R	N	E	T	Z	E	R	
L		P		D		T		A		F		D
A	V	E	R	A	G	E		T	I	T	L	E
S		R		L		R		I				P
W	E	S	T		F		C	O	O	P	E	R
E		O		N	O	L	A	N		O		E
G	U	N	N	E	R		P		U	S	E	S
I				D		D		T		T		S
A	W	A	R	D		A	D	E	L	P	H	I
N		L		O		V		A		O		O
	J	A	R	I	L	I	T	M	A	N	E	N
		N		G		D		S		E		

No. 42

E		C		B	R	I	A	N	H	A	L	L
I	R	O	N			E		B		E		O
N		L			A	Q	U	A	R	I	U	S
T	A	L	L	E	C		S		O		T	
R		Y			T		I			O		U
A	R	M	E	D		E	V	E	R	T	O	N
C		O			J	O	E			S		D
H	A	R	D	M	A	N		Z	I	E	G	E
T		E			M		L			M		R
	D		W		A		O	X	F	O	R	D
N	I	N	E	T	I	E	S			B		O
	D		A		C		E		D	O	U	G
R	I	C	K	P	A	R	R	Y		R		S

No. 43

		P	O	R	T	S	M	O	U	T	H	
K		L		A		A		P		R		S
I	T	A	L	I	A	N		P	O	I	N	T
R		Y		N		D		O		P		A
K	I	E	V		D	E	A	N		S	O	N
P		R		U		R		E				L
A	R	S	E	N	E		I	N	S	I	D	E
T				B		A		T		N		Y
R	E	S		E	A	S	T		S	T	E	P
I		K		A		R		W		E		A
C	O	U	R	T		O	C	O	N	N	O	R
K		L		E		M		O		S		K
	A	L	A	N	W	A	D	D	L	E		

No. 44

	F	R	O	D	E		B	R	O	W	N	
P		O		U		S		E		A		K
R	I	G	H	T		C	H	A	R	L	I	E
E		E		C		O		L		L		V
N	O	R	T	H	E	R	N		J	A	R	I
T				M		E		C		C		N
O	L	D	H	A	M		C	H	E	E	R	S
N		I		N		P		A				H
P	I	E	S		L	A	W	R	E	N	C	E
A		T		I		Y		L		E		E
R	A	M	S	D	E	N		T	I	R	E	D
K		A		O		E		O		V		Y
	D	R	I	L	L		K	N	E	E	S	

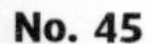

No. 45

I	A	N	R	U	S	H		T		D		
	L		E		I		G	R	E	E	N	
W	A	N	D	E	R	S		I		A		
	N		D		O		C	O	R	N	E	R
O	W	N	E	R			H				I	
	A		V		C		E		L	O	G	O
	D		I	S	R	A	E	L	I		H	
I	D	O	L		E		R		T		T	
	L				W			E	M	L	Y	N
N	E	S	S	I	E		H		A		F	
		T		T		J	O	H	N	S	O	N
	M	E	L	I	A		P		E		U	
		P		S		B	E	R	N	A	R	D

No. 46

T	I	R	O	L		P		T		H		C
U			V		T	H	R	E	E	O	N	E
N	I	G	E	L		I		A		M		N
N			R	A	Y	L	A	M	B	E	R	T
E		T		C				S		G		R
L	O	O	S	E	N	E	D		D	A	V	E
		M		S		G		P		M		
P	A	G	E		F	O	U	R	T	E	E	N
R		R		M				E		S		I
I	V	A	N	A	L	O	N	S	O			N
D		C		N		W		S	P	I	C	E
A	V	I	C	O	H	E	N		E			T
Y		E		R		N		E	N	T	R	Y

No. 47

		T		S		I		A		C		
B	A	R	N	E	Y	R	U	B	B	L	E	
O		A		V		I		I		U		J
B	A	N	N	E	R	S		L	I	B	R	A
P		M		N		H		I				C
A	B	E	L		K		A	T	T	A	C	K
I		R		E	A	R	L	Y		V		B
S	P	E	E	D	Y		F		U	E	F	A
L				I		P		A		R		L
E	L	E	C	T		E	P	H	R	A	I	M
Y		X		I		R		E		G		E
	J	A	S	O	N	M	C	A	T	E	E	R
		M		N		S		D		S		

No. 48

P		M		M	C	M	A	N	A	M	A	N
R	A	C	E		I		C		L		L	
O		D			S	A	M	H	A	R	D	Y
G	L	O	V	E	S		I		N		O	
R		U			E		L			H		O
A	N	G	E	R		C	A	R	D	I	F	F
M		A			B	A	N			B		T
M	I	L	K	C	U	P		C	Z	E	C	H
E		L			R		A			R		E
	H		S		R		R	O	O	N	E	Y
P	O	S	T	P	O	N	E			I		E
	P		U		W		N		G	A	L	A
W	E	D	N	E	S	D	A	Y		N		R

No. 49

		C	O	L	I	N	I	R	W	I	N	
I		H		E		E		O		A		N
P	R	E	S	C	O	T		C	O	N	T	I
S		Y		H		T		H		S		N
W	A	R	M		H	E	A	D		T	I	E
I		O		S		D		A				T
C	O	U	N	T	Y		S	L	O	P	P	Y
H				R		C		E		R		T
T	O	P		I	V	A	N		T	O	S	H
O		R		K		N		S		M		R
W	H	I	T	E		A	W	E	S	O	M	E
N		C		R		R		M		T		E
	M	E	R	S	E	Y	S	I	D	E		

No. 50

	G	E	O	F	F		W	A	L	S	H	
I		R		L		D		R		O		C
P	O	R	T	O		I	A	N	R	U	S	H
S		O		O		O		E		N		A
W	O	R	L	D	C	U	P		H	E	L	L
I				L		F		D		S		L
C	E	L	T	I	C		J	E	S	S	I	E
H		I		T		C		F				N
T	I	N	Y		C	H	E	E	R	I	N	G
O		D		S		A		N		R		E
W	E	S	T	H	A	M		D	E	W	A	R
N		A		I		P		E		I		S
	B	Y	R	N	E		B	R	U	N	O	

L.F.C.

WALK ALONE

Notes

L.F.C.

WALK ALONE

Notes

L.F.C.

WALK ALONE

Notes